M

Jenny Angell spent th[...]
priced callgirl in Bo[...]
people that she met du[...]
to write about the exp[erience.] Jenny is now happily married and lives in New England, where she
continues to write.

For further information about Jenny Angell, visit
her website at www.jeannetteangell.com

Visit www.AuthorTracker.co.uk for exclusive
updates on Jenny Angell.

By the same author

Callgirl

JENNY ANGELL

Madam

AVON

AVON

A division of HarperCollins*Publishers*
77–85 Fulham Palace Road,
London W6 8JB

www.harpercollins.co.uk

This paperback edition 2008
1

First published in the U.S.A by
The Permanent Press, New York, NY, 2005

Copyright © Jenny Angell 2008

Jenny Angell asserts the moral right to
be identified as the author of this work

A catalogue record for this book is
available from the British Library

ISBN: 978-1-84756-066-7

Set in Minion by Thomson Digital

Printed and bound in Great Britain by
Clays Ltd, St Ives plc

FSC is a non-profit international organisation established to promote the
responsible management of the world's forests. Products carrying the FSC
label are independently certified to assure consumers that they come
from forests that are managed to meet the social, economic and
ecological needs of present and future generations.

Find out more about HarperCollins and the environment at
www.harpercollins.co.uk/green

Thanks as always to my husband, to my literary agents (Philip Spitzer, Lukas Ortiz, and Jane Judd), and to the wonderful editors at Avon/HarperCollins in London: Keshini Naidoo and Sammia Rafique. And thanks especially to Peach: this book is both for and about you, and all the fragile and lovely spirits we've known together.

This is a second-hand memoir, written about a person other than myself. Because of that, and because of the necessity of protecting people's identities, particularly Peach, it can be viewed as true but not completely factual.

Most people in this book are composites. Most places have been changed. While I spent countless hours with Peach talking about this book, listening to her stories and thoughts and her feelings, I cannot guarantee the accuracy of anything that is written here that does not include me directly.

Readers are urged to take it as it is meant – as an example of living a life that many people could otherwise not imagine, and yet one that is familiar in enough ways to perhaps help people see that we are not so different from each other, after all.

For Peach, of course

AUTHOR'S NOTE

Some time ago, I was a callgirl and "Peach" was my madam. This is her story as told to me.

The names of people, places, times, and other details have been changed. I personally witnessed some of the events described in this book. Other descriptions are based on what "Peach" and others told me.

CONTENTS

Contents

PROLOGUE

For three years of my life, I worked as a callgirl. I worked for a woman-owned and woman-operated escort service, and that agency is what made those three years more than just an emergency financial stopgap. It became, instead, an interesting and empowering experience for me.

I wrote my story of those years in a memoir titled *Callgirl*. And because the madam I worked for figured so importantly in that story, I decided to share what one madam's life is like. It's Peach's turn; this is her story.

RENDEZVOUS

The couple had been sipping wine for almost half an hour when he made his first move.

They had already exhausted talk of his work (he was an accountant, so that part didn't take too long) and hers (she was a graduate student, she told him, though when you purchase companionship through an escort service you never know whether you're being told the truth), and he had been watching the ample cleavage defined by the black lace camisole long enough to be feeling excited. Very excited.

Still, he liked the sound of her voice, and he listened to it longer than he had planned.

He took the wineglass from her hand, gently, courteously, and placed it on the glass top of the coffee table in front of them. She was smiling. When he kissed her, her lips were as warm and yielding as he had thought they would be.

She put her arms around him and drew him in closer, her mouth, her lips against his, her tongue exploring inside his mouth, feeling hot, feeling impatient. He sensed a surge, a response inside himself, as though his groin were suddenly on fire.

She leaned back on the bed and pulled him on top of her, still fully dressed, and her legs came up and encircled him, pulling him down harder on top of her. She was kissing him back, his face, his neck, pulling at his clothes even as she held him pinned on top of her; it was as though a fire had been ignited inside of her when he made his first move. *She must like me*, he thought, as he returned her kisses, reaching between their two bodies to fondle her breasts. *She must really be hot for me.*

She gasped and pulled away from him, scrambling up further on the bed, still with that smile. Slowly, watching him, she started to undress. The black lace top that barely concealed the camisole, the skirt … she was wearing a garter belt and stockings – he caught his breath and felt that pulsing in his cock again. *She knows what I want*, he thought, and locking eyes with her, he stood up, unbuckled his belt, and unzipped his khakis.

She was just wearing the camisole and stockings now, no underpants – *God, I love it when they don't wear anything underneath* – and she leaned back against the headboard, still watching him, her legs

4

falling apart naturally. Slowly, she put a finger in her mouth, then withdrew it; slowly, she moved her hand down and slid the same finger into her pussy.

She's so hot, he thought. He pulled off his shirt. He couldn't take his eyes off her pussy. She didn't shave it, like some girls did, and he was fascinated with the curly dark hair and the slender hand on it, moving, pulsing …

He crawled up to be with her, but she put one elegant, black-stockinged leg up, her foot against his chest, to hold him away from her. Her eyes were still holding his. She wet her finger once more and started really caressing herself, rocking her hips rhythmically, moving against her hand, her breathing coming faster, even moaning, and all the while her eyes were still on him.

He felt like his cock was going to burst.

She paused and then asked, her voice low, "Do you want me?"

Oh, God, like no one I've ever wanted before. "Yes," he managed to say, licking his lips. "Yes, yes, I want you!"

The hand went to the nightstand. "Put this on," she whispered, passing him the foil packet. He complied, fumbling with it a little, watching as she went back to touching herself, *she's getting ahead of me*, he thought, and then it was on, finally it was on, and she slowly – too slowly, too slowly! – moved the foot that was holding him back from her, extending the leg gracefully to the side, her arms now up and open, pulling him down on her.

He fumbled for another moment, his cock in his hand, and then he was sliding inside her, fast, hard, and she moaned again. She was kissing his face, kissing his neck, his ear – and then she bit his ear, hard. He gasped, but she only whispered, "You're so good …" before tipping her head back, her eyes finally closed, moaning as she moved with him.

She was soft and yielding and magnificent. He drove his cock into her pussy, again and again and again, feeling the fire building, feeling it engulf not only his groin, but then, suddenly, unexpectedly, his whole body – *Christ,* he thought, *I'm on fire* – and then he was coming, again and again and again, feeling it wash over him like waves, putting out the fire, leaving him weak, exhausted, and empty.

She didn't hurry him, like some of them did. Finally, she slid out from under him and padded into the bathroom. He heard water running, and a few moments later she was back, a washcloth in her hand.

She moved him onto his back without saying a word, removed the condom, and used the washcloth on him. It was warm and wet, just like she had been. When she was finished, she lay down next to him, her head on his chest, her fingers slowly, lazily caressing him.

He started drifting off. He saw a farmhouse and a well next to it, fragments of some dream he'd been having the night before resurfacing as he drifted into a sleepier state, lulled by her warmth next to him and her fingertips on his body.

The telephone rang.

He jerked awake, aware suddenly of the hotel room, the woman next to him, the shrilling of the phone. It was his room, so he reached for it. *Christ, that's loud!* "Hello?" he managed to say at last.

The voice on the other end managed to be both gentle and cheerful. "Craig, hi, this is Peach."

He rolled over so that he was sitting on the edge of the bed. "Hi, Peach."

"Can I talk to her?"

"Sure." The girl was next to him; he handed her the phone. "Hi, Peach," she said easily, and then listened for a moment. "Yes, I enjoyed it." She reached over and took his hand, winking at him as she said it. "Anytime he calls again, I'd love to see him." Another short pause. "Okay, thanks, Peach. Bye."

She hung up the phone, put her arms around him, and kissed him again. That was unusual, too. "I had a lovely time," she said, softly.

"You mean that?" *She probably says it to everyone. Still, I really felt that she liked me.*

"No," she said softly. "Only when it's true."

She moved away, pulled on her skirt and blouse, and he realized with a start that that was all she had taken off. He's had girls nude in the first five minutes who hadn't gotten him off like this one had. *This is going to be embarrassing,* he thought. *Here goes …*

"Um," he said, "I'd like to see you again."

She was running fingertips through her long red hair, tangled now. "I'd like that, too," she said, softly.

"But —" *Just say it.* "Umm … I'm sorry, I forgot your name."

To his surprise, she grinned, a wide spontaneous smile. "That's okay," she said. "Sometimes I forget it myself." She had on her black blazer and little black handbag that had been on the nightstand, where she had put the condoms. She came over to where he was still sitting, with just his pants pulled up haphazardly, and kissed the top of his head. "Tia," she said. "My name is Tia."

"Tia," he said. *That name suits her. Maybe she's Italian.*

She kissed him again. "I have to go," she said. "Call Peach and ask for me."

"I will," he said.

She started for the door, then suddenly turned, came back quickly, bent down, and gave him a full, deep, wet kiss on the mouth. A lot of the girls never did that, and especially not once they were leaving;

8

there was a depressing postcoital efficiency in the profession that he found irritating. "Soon," she whispered. "Please call soon."

He started to say something, then cleared his throat. "I will," he managed, "I will."

She closed the hotel room door behind her and walked down the carpeted corridor. Waiting for the elevator, she once again fixed her hair with her fingertips, and straightened her skirt. By the time she emerged into the lobby she looked cool, collected, and still very sexy.

She went to the bank of phones located to the left of the front desk, put in coins that she had ready in her blazer pocket, and called me. "Peach? It's Jenny. I'm done."

"Great." I mentally checked my roster of potential clients for the night. "Do you want another call?"

The woman in the hotel lobby stifled a yawn. "Not really. Only if it's one of my regulars," she said. "I have some reading to catch up on."

"Okay, then," I said. There was another call coming in. "Hey, honey, call me when you get home, okay? Maybe we can have lunch tomorrow."

"Sure thing. Talk to you then."

I disconnected her call and picked up the one that was waiting. "Hello?"

"Hey, Peach, it's Crystal. I'm here with Mark."

"Great, honey," I said, checking the clock. "I'll call you out in an hour."

"Sure thing."

I stretched and looked around for my novels and magazines. Always need my novels. It looked like it was going to be a busy night.

WORKING THE PHONES

The telephone was ringing.

That's not unusual: in my world, the telephone is always ringing. It's an occupational hazard. I don't suppose that I should complain; I'm the one, after all, who has the advertisements in the local alternative newspaper asking people to call me. I'm the one who persuades guys to use my number, to see my girls, to become, in an odd, indescribable way, my friend. It's my lifeline, the telephone.

But sometimes – once in a while – I do find myself wishing that it would just stop.

It was ringing this morning while I was trying to get Sam ready for his day. Yes: I am a madam, and I also have a child. It's not an oxymoron; it's my life. I checked the caller ID and saw that it was a new client, someone I'd sent a couple of girls to in the last few days. That kind of regularity translates as Very Good Client. "Hi, Gary."

11

"Peach?" He sounded surprised that I knew who he was. As though he hadn't heard about the latest in telephone technology. Although, to be fair, I've always been very good with numbers, and I'd matched the cell phone display to his name almost instantaneously. "Hi, Peach. Um – I was just, you know, thinking about what you said last night, and you're right, I need to get out of my rut."

Great. And now you want to talk about it. "That's probably a good idea, Gary." I was hunting for one of Sam's missing shoes as I waited for the rest. I already knew what it was going to be about. When one of my clients says he wants to get out of a rut, he's not talking about changing jobs, going on vacation, or taking up a new hobby.

My clients are much more specific than that.

"Well, you know what you said, about trying something new, and I guess that I just had this kind of fixation with blondes, you know, but I think ..." He paused and took a deep breath, as though entering into an important pact, making a difficult commitment. "I think I'm ready for a change."

I was watching the clock. The school bus waits for no madam. "Gary, that's terrific. But can you call me back later? I've got a new girl working tonight. I think you'll really like her. We can connect you once she checks in."

12

"What's she like, Peach?"

I sighed. I should have known I wasn't going to get him off the phone that easily. "She's got dark hair, five-seven, 122 pounds, 36-26-32. She's gorgeous, Gary, and she's really sweet."

"What's her name?"

Thinking fast, I said, "April. I'll have her call you as soon as she checks in, does that work for you? She's a college student. She's in class right now."

"Oh. Okay, Peach."

No "Thank you, Peach," or anything like that. Silly me, to expect courtesies from someone who calls an escort service at breakfast time just to chat. I frowned at the phone as I pressed the off button. April. I'd have to remember that.

Most of the girls who work for me use fictional names. I can't blame them – after all, I do the same thing – but sometimes it's a little tough keeping them straight. Especially when I assign one on the spur of the moment, as I just had.

In the kitchen, Sam was voicing his displeasure with the menu choices. I sighed and marched in to head him off before he decided to throw the offending food around. Now all I had to do was figure out who the hell I had that I could pass off as this April, who was, unfortunately, a total figment of my imagination.

* * * * * *

Sometimes I think I'm in the wrong profession altogether.

Mornings, in particular, are tough. I'm not supposed to be working then – we do most of our work in the late afternoons and at night – but I still answer the calls: it would be suicidal not to. Talking with Gary this morning hadn't precisely made my day, but yesterday was worse. It was raining for the third day in a row, my husband was away, and Sam was adamantly refusing to eat the exact same breakfast he had loved only the day before.

And I had a new girl on the phone, asking for advice.

"Peach, should I get the wax done just before I go? Sometimes my skin is a little irritated right after I have a wax. And – there's this other thing: what do you think – should I have *all* the hair removed, or leave a strip of it on?"

Wonderful. I haven't had my first cup of coffee yet, and here I'm talking to this girl about her pubic hair. Ask me if I *care*.

Well, actually, the reality is that I do. I do care about these girls and I care about making things as comfortable for them as I can and I care about their confidence (if not, precisely, about their wax jobs); but sometimes it just gets a little ... overwhelming. Like

14

I'm a nanny with a particularly difficult and demanding set of charges.

The only difference between us is that *my* charges
are all drop-dead gorgeous and in their twenties. The
rest? I'd say it pretty much stays the same.

* * * * * *

Despite what you may be thinking after reading all
of this, most of the time, I love what I do. I love owning my own business. I love having my days free. For
a long time, I loved the cachet that went along with
being a successful madam in a relatively small city
where everyone who is anyone knows everybody else.
I loved the entrée it gave me to events and parties and
inner circles; I loved being seen as someone who people wanted to be seen with.

And then there's the issue of power. After all, my
profession involves providing something that men
want, and I'm the gatekeeper. I'm the one who gives or
doesn't give what they are asking for. There are days
when that feels pretty good.

This book is partly about that, partly about what
it was like to be flashy and successful in a glittering
world where it was always night, where the real world
was somewhere else. Because that was a big part of my
life. But it's also about how that gets old, finally; about
how the other side to the nightlife can be devastating

and even deadly; about how, in a sense, I grew out of it and into something that is just as satisfying in a completely different way.

And, through it all, I ran – and continue to run – a very successful escort business.

THE MAKING OF A MADAM

I didn't start out wanting to be a madam.

I mean, it's not the kind of career choice that little girls consider when they talk together about what they're going to be when they grow up. Let's see: teacher, nurse, lawyer, bordello owner ... nope, just doesn't work. There are some careers that you choose, and some careers that choose you. This one definitely falls into the latter category.

So, how does a nice girl like me end up running an escort service?

I'm not sure exactly where to start. I could use all the excuses that people generally use when they're trying to justify what others may see as questionable behavior. I could talk about boyfriends and about wanting to do well at Boston's Emerson College; about my parents' expectations that I would marry and buy a mock Tudor house somewhere in the suburbs. I could list my various jobs, give you a resumé or a list of recommendations; I could self-righteously mention exactly how few positions are available to people when they first leave a school like Emerson, which is so specialized in communications and acting and related fields. I could even say that I had put a lot of thought into it and decided that running an escort service would make me Businesswoman of the Year.

But the reality is different. The reality is that I was tired of coming home to the guy I was living with (for no reason other than that we had started living together and inertia had taken over) who did nothing but smoke pot and watch television. I was tired of looking for jobs in communications with a degree in Communications that meant absolutely nothing at the end of the day. I was tired, tired, tired …

I did try to follow one of the roads that lead to what others see as respectable careers. I tried sales first. I've always been pretty good at talking people into things, so I went to work in the sales area of some low-income housing developments on the edge of North Cambridge, Massachusetts, and moonlighted answering the telephone for the maintenance department. The first clue I had that I was in the wrong place was when a couple of the guys refused to fix the toilet in a certain tenant's apartment. The tenant in question didn't speak English, so I started giving the maintenance guys holy hell about discriminating against him.

When one of them could finally get a word in, it was to say, "You know, lady, no one's gonna go there. Two other maintenance guys almost got killed fixing stuff for that creep."

Oh.

The second clue came when the news trucks all started coming around and people began shoving microphones in my face, asking me questions about the guy on the eighteenth floor who had just gotten arrested for running a prostitution ring out of his apartment.

And all of that – those events, those situations that I can single out and point to – didn't even touch the sheer bleakness of working there, in that world, with people who had lost every shred of hope they had ever had for a better life. Poverty is a grinding, daily, hurtful thing, and after a generation of it, most people cannot imagine a world that doesn't involve welfare, or dealing drugs, or stints in prison, or wanting something with the only part of you that hasn't accepted that you'll never be able to have it. I know I'm a hypocrite to feel that way and not become a social worker, or something – anything to help ease people's pain. Instead, I decided one thing: I wasn't going to make a career out of being part of anybody's misery. I wanted a modicum of happiness in my work.

So I made some New Year's resolutions in the middle of the summer and kicked the boyfriend out and thought for a while about my assets – what is fashionable, these days, to call a skills set. And I realized right away that what I'm good at – what I'm brilliant at – is *talking*. I can talk anybody into anything. I can sweet-talk operators into giving me information they never planned to give out. I've always had this big double bed and I sit there with my telephone and my Yellow Pages and man, I'm all set. I can get just about anything I need with my phone and my Yellow Pages.

On the other hand, what do people do who are good on the telephone? I certainly didn't want to do telemarketing. Yuck. Interrupting people having dinner to try and sell them subscriptions to some magazine they'd never read anyway. It just didn't work for me.

So I sat and called everyone I knew and didn't get any closer to figuring out what to do with my so-called career. I took a couple of temp jobs working as a receptionist for high-tech companies and resigned myself to doing something like that in the foreseeable future.

When I finally happened on the ad in the newspaper – almost accidentally, on a day I had not set aside for job-hunting – I had no idea that it was going to change my life forever.

* * * * * *

Laura lived out in one of Boston's suburbs – Wilmington, was it? Or maybe Lynnfield? – someplace like that, that's what I remember. And even though my departed boyfriend hadn't been good for much, he *had* managed to pay half the rent. Now I was struggling to manage it by myself. Come work for me, Laura said, and you can stay in my basement.

It sounded pretty good to me. Work and a place to stay, just when I needed both. I said yes. I didn't consider what people would think when they learned I was working for an escort service, even in the minor role of receptionist. I didn't consider much of anything. This is probably typical of many of the women who work in the profession: it seems like an answer to a prayer, a way to make ends meet, a way to make a living, for heaven's sake. And when the reactions trickle in, we're always surprised by them.

I didn't think about people's reactions. I just went to work for Laura.

My first impression was how clean it was: everything was impeccable. Laura ran an escort service that was both in-call and out-call: some girls went out to clients' homes; others saw the guys there, at Laura's place. It was never called a bordello. In fact, in all my years in the business, I've never heard an in-call place called a bordello. We just called it Laura's. Maybe it's just a Boston thing.

So I finally had a job. I was the receptionist; I greeted clients and took all the telephone calls. And listened to the bickering.

"The sheets have to be clean," Laura kept saying to the girls. That was her constant mantra. You wouldn't think that clean sheets could ever become such an issue. Whose turn it was to change the sheets, who had last used the front room, who had done the laundry yesterday. That was all that the girls talked about: those damned sheets.

The sheets weren't my department. I got to talk to the guys.

The clients came in all shapes and sizes, both figuratively and literally. Guys who knew exactly what they wanted, and guys who could be talked into seeing the girl who hadn't had a call for two days. Young guys that you couldn't figure out, for the life of you, why they couldn't get a date on their own; and older men who clearly had no other recourse, even in Boston's comparatively laid-back sexual climate.

I got good at working the phones, and I got good at it fast. You had to – they'd keep you on the line all night, otherwise. "You have a great voice – you sure I can't see you? What do you look like? What are you wearing right now?" I got good at deflecting them, just the right edge of flirtatiousness in my voice, just the right edge of business. When I didn't work, and Laura did the phones, the clients complained. "Where's Abby?"

I was sleeping on a foldout sofa in her finished basement, sharing the room with an old foosball table and some castoff furniture and lamps from the bedrooms upstairs. That was just fine with me. I had a bank account, and every week I had more money to put into it – the eventual deposit on an apartment somewhere closer to the city than Wilmington.

Because, to tell you the truth, when I wasn't working, I was bored.

Well, that's not entirely true. I did have a car that ran most of the time, and when it was running there were a lot of things to do. It was summer, so I could go into Boston and sit on the Common or in the Public Gardens; in the fall I could go out to Concord and walk around Walden Pond. I could go to Lansdowne Street in town on my nights off and hang out in the clubs. But all of it, all the time, I did alone.

I really didn't know very many people. To be honest, on a day-to-day basis, I was fairly lonely. I didn't have much of a social life. I worked nights, for one thing. And for another ... well, all of my friends from college were starting their careers, or had moved away, or gotten married, or something. I felt a little bereft, as if some train had already pulled out of the station and I had just then realized that I was supposed to be on it.

At Laura's, though, I wasn't bored. Here, things were always hopping. Guys stopping in, talking and laughing with me in the living room while they were passing the time before their "date" was free, the girls sitting around waiting to be chosen. It was a cattle call, and as a good feminist I wasn't altogether comfortable with it. But it was money, extraordinarily good money. And it was more than that – okay, I'll admit it: it really was exciting. As if I were on the cutting edge of something slightly risqué, slightly dangerous, slightly naughty. As, of course, I was.

I guess the best thing to compare that feeling to is going out at night to the bars, the clubs. How you dance around when you're getting ready to go out. How you have that little edge of excitement when you first get there, not knowing exactly what you'll find, who you'll meet. The tension. And then, when you do strike up a conversation, the flirting, the games, the playfulness and mystery, and the newness of it all. And if it goes well, holding the guy in your power, deciding whether you're going to sleep with him or not, deciding how far you're going to let him go, deciding if you're going to be nice to him or cut him down. All that power, and instead of getting dressed up and going looking for it, *it came to me.* And I got paid for it. It was my job to be hip and seductive – and unattainable.

"Hello?"

"Yeah, um, I wanted to, um –"

"Make an appointment?" Sweet and seductive.

"Um, yeah."

"When did you want to come by, sir?" Can't start by asking for a name – it spooked them. He would say tonight.

"Tonight? Now?"

"That's fine. I just need to get a little information, sir." Pretty voice now, nonthreatening. "I need your name and phone number, and I'll call you right back."

"Why?"

"It's for everyone's protection, sir. Then I can give you directions."

He relaxed. There was something about that promise that always did it. "Okay. Ed Lawrence. 555-1324."

"I'll call you right back, Ed."

After that, it was easy. Directions. Sometimes they'd want to keep me on the phone, run down what they called the "menu," but I learned how to handle that gracefully as well. "I'm sure that one of the young ladies will suit you, sir." They always did; the guy just wanted the thrill of prolonging the phone call. His goal was for it to last; mine was to close the deal and move on. Usually I won.

One night Laura had a late arrival. I was asleep downstairs, and she thought – well, I don't honestly know *what* she was thinking. Maybe none of the girls were around. Maybe she figured that he was easy and I wouldn't mind. Whatever was going through her little brain, she sent him down to me.

Big mistake.

First of all, I had never planned on a career in prostitution from anything other than an administrative point of view. Second of all, I was asleep. Third of all, the guy liked to give oral sex, which is why I think she sent him downstairs to me: the scenario would be, he'd go down, I'd never even have to completely wake up, he'd go back upstairs, pay, and leave. What neither Laura nor her client had counted on was the yeast infection I was treating at the time. Her little client went down, all right – and I woke up to this face looming above me, literally foaming at the mouth.

I don't know which one of us was more freaked out.

And so my career as a call girl ended as soon as it had – albeit involuntarily – begun. But I learned a lot that year I spent doing the phones and working the desk for Laura. I learned about the specifics of running a business like hers, about what worked and what didn't. I learned about clients and employees and the world's perception of what we did. I learned a lot about power – about my power.

And most importantly, I learned that I could do it better than her.

So I took my almost-working car and my revived bank account, rented an apartment in Boston's trendy Bay Village, and opened up my own business. That was nineteen years ago. I've been doing it ever since.

* * * * * *

I chose the name Peach from a short story.

It's as good a source as any for finding a name, I suppose. But it also is weird, in a Twilight Zone kind of way, because the person who wrote that story later came to work for me for a couple of years. What are the chances of that happening? They must be a million to one.

What I didn't want, above all, was to use my own name. I didn't want the guys asking for Abby, or knowing anything about Abby. From the very beginning, I wanted an element of deniability to it all. I wanted to both be and not be this new persona.

So I became Peach.

I knew I had to keep my working life and my personal life very, very separate. To my friends and family, I would be Abby. To my girls and my clients, I'd be Peach. And that's worked pretty well for me.

Which is not to say that I latched onto it right away. If I can sit here and talk calmly about having a family, having a business, juggling them the way any working mother does, you need to know that it didn't come to me naturally.

In fact, for a whole lot of years, I was much more Peach than I was Abby. Sometimes I think I got a little lost in being Peach … so that's part of what this story is about. Getting lost.

And getting found.

LOSSES

The door opened slowly, too slowly. The faces were grave.

I was pressed up against the wall in the corridor, scarcely daring to breathe. There was a very expensive vase on the table next to me, from some Chinese dynasty that's remembered in the Western world only for its porcelain. I had been told to never touch the vase.

The voices inside the room had gone on for far too long, a steady murmur, the murmur of death.

Now the door was opening, and they were all coming out. My mother, her face red and blotchy from crying. Dr. Copeland. Two of my father's business associates.

Dr. Copeland saw me first and, ignoring the other people – which was very unlike a grown-up – came over and squatted in the hallway next to me. "Abby," he said, gently, "how long have you been here?"

I stifled a sob. "Forever," I said. I felt that if I said anything more than that, I'd start crying, and it had been made clear to me that I was not to cry.

He didn't go away, as I expected him to. He put a hand on my shoulder, instead. "You're going to need to be a brave girl, Abby."

"Yes, sir, I know."

He frowned, as though that was the wrong answer. "But you can be brave and feel sad at the same time," he said.

I glanced at my mother. She was standing with the light from the window behind her, and all I could see was her thin elegant outline. Her arms were crossed.

I didn't have to see her face; I already knew what the expression was.

I looked back into the doctor's kindly eyes with a quick indrawn breath and a little bit of panic. "I'll be brave," I assured him. Maybe if I said what he wanted me to say, he'd go away and not say things that made me want to cry.

He didn't go away.

Instead, he scrunched down and sat on the floor next to me. I clearly heard my mother's disapproving intake of breath, and stiffened, but she didn't say anything. "Abby," said Dr. Copeland, "you know that your daddy is very sick."

No one had ever called him Daddy before, except me. My mother always prefaced references to him with "Your father." I nodded.

He nodded, too, as though we had just shared a very deep secret. "Abby, I'm afraid that he's going to die."

My heart thudded, and I thought suddenly that I might throw up. I shouldn't, I knew that I shouldn't, but I wondered how I could keep it from happening. What can you do? Swallow it all back? I didn't say anything and swallowed hard, and the feeling receded. Dr. Copeland squeezed my shoulders. "We're all going to miss your daddy," he said, "but do you know what, Abby? I think that you're going to miss him most of all."

I didn't know how to respond, so I didn't say anything.

The doctor gave me one last firm pat on the back and stood up, with some difficulty. One of my father's business associates gave him a hand. My mother never moved.

Their voices faded away down the hallway and the big sweeping staircase that led downstairs. I stayed where I was, looking longingly at the closed door.

"Abby!" my mother called, her voice sharp. "Come downstairs now!"

I suppose that I went. I was good that way. Obedient.

I never saw my daddy again.

LEAVING MOTHER SUPERIOR

When I left Laura's place, I had only the faintest idea how to make things work.

What I mean is, I knew what I *didn't* want. In retrospect, maybe that's a pretty good place to start.

I didn't want to run an in-call service. That was the first decision. For a whole lot of reasons, I didn't want in-call.

First of all, there was the risk associated with it. There's always more risk when you have an actual physical place where something illegal is going on. But there was the intrusion, as well, the sense of never quite knowing where work ends and Real Life begins. Laura's house was – well, Laura's house. For Laura, my one and only role model in the business, there had never been a clear line between the two. If I didn't make a distinction, it's because she never did: her work was her life. I wanted my own space. I wanted my own life.

You have to understand something about this woman: this is someone who made arrangements for her son to get laid when he was fifteen. She sent one of her girls to him in his own bedroom, which was, incidentally, just up the stairs from where the girls all worked. Now that's one hell of a birthday present from your mother.

I remember one Christmas party – Laura always threw these incredibly extravagant parties – watching her son dancing with the girls with a champagne glass in his hand and an erection in his pants. The girls took off more and more of their clothes as the evening wore on, and Chris was there, right in the middle of it all. He was loving it, of course, but I couldn't help thinking that his time would have been better spent making out in the back seat of a car somewhere.

There was something about the way Laura dealt with Chris that seemed wrong, really wrong, to me. I realize that many people – maybe even most people – think that sex workers have no ethics, no morals, no code of conduct. Well, I do. I may differ with other people on the definition of that code, but I have one all the same.

Not that I ever had much in common with Laura: we're both madams; and that is pretty much where the resemblance ends.

She was prissy about cleanliness, as I mentioned, to the point of covering all her furniture in plastic, just like they used to do in the 1950s. ("Well," she said to me once, as though it were the most logical thing in the world, "you never know who's going to sit there, or what they're going to do." Yuck. I don't *ever* want to not know what people are doing on my living room sofa). And yet this prissy housekeeper regularly freebased, leaving all sorts of paraphernalia around in her kitchen – aluminum foil, cigarette ashes, little gram bags of coke.

She was organized beyond belief, keeping this small notebook, adding up, who owed what to whom every night. Yet she couldn't be bothered with all the work that went into brewing coffee and always drank hers instant.

Laura was, suffice it to say, a study in contrasts.

This showed up in the way she worked, too. She was extremely stupendously generous to her girls, giving them gifts at unexpected moments, singling one or another out and taking her on a surprise shopping spree. Once, she took eight of the girls on a trip to Alaska all expenses paid. It was work, of course, a road show of sorts, but they made absolutely fantastic money and got to travel on top of it.

But she demanded – required – fanatical loyalty. You didn't work for anybody else while you were working for Laura. Period. She'd cut you off; there were no second chances. And she would invariably find out, because everybody knows everybody else in

Boston. A client would usually tip her off – most of the clients were hooked into more than one service. If they called another agency and got someone they'd already met through Laura, they told her. And that was that.

It was as if Laura had this little circle of nuns around her, going off to do their assigned tasks (in this case, fucking men for money) and then returning docilely to the convent under their madam mother superior's sphere of influence. She didn't like any of them – including me – having friendships outside of the house. She sure as hell didn't like any of us having boyfriends outside of the house.

These rules, such as they were, were never articulated, but we all understood them, and we all used them against each other.

I've never *ever* seen such a bunch of gossips as I saw in that house – and where I come from, gossiping is an art form. These girls were *impressive*. Well, it was only natural that we would gossip: there we all were, stuck in this nouveau-riche house in the back of beyond in suburbia, hanging out together all day with very little to do. No wonder all we talked about was laundry and each other. We probably sounded like junior high kids whispering and giggling by their lockers in a school corridor.

I take that back. We were worse than junior high kids. At least they have the excuse of age, inexperience, and innocence. None of us had any of that going for us.

We were all in our twenties, everyone (except me) dressed in lingerie of some kind, made up, nails lacquered, sitting around on the plastic-covered furniture, waiting. We'd keep the soaps on all day, until a client pulled up outside; then the TV had to be turned off. Major rule, that.

A guy would come in, and everyone would suddenly try to look like it's a normal thing, all these girls sitting around in their lace and satin and high heels, each one of them competing with the next for his attention.

If that doesn't make you want to do drugs, I don't know what would.

If the guy had an appointment with someone, then that was different. Everyone would smile sweetly and the girl would take him off to one of the bedrooms. We'd switch the television back on as soon as we heard the door shut. These were the days before the Internet: we couldn't just look up what we'd missed on the soaps, so clients were a major interruption.

When we weren't watching TV, we were talking about anything and everything, but mostly about each other – and Laura. Lord, we gossiped about Laura, and we were vicious – who she was seeing (Laura was always seeing someone), how much coke she'd done the night before, and what she'd said somebody had said about somebody else. I remember, years later, seeing a high school rendition of *The Music Man*, and being absolutely amazed at how well Rogers and Hammerstein had described our activity.

Of course, the first thing that everyone wanted to do was find Laura and report back to her on who had said what.

In some ways, I guess, I do see some of Laura in myself. We can both be incredibly generous and incredibly selfish. We both have a lot of issues that we deal with by not dealing with them. We both talk – a lot, probably too much. We both manage to survive.

But her style never was my style, and when I left her house and got myself my dream apartment in Boston's Bay Village, I knew that I had learned enough to know what I *didn't* want.

That was a damned good start.

* * * * * *

At that time, the *Boston Phoenix* had a pullout adult section called "After Dark." It still has this section, actually, but these days it's been renamed and redesigned, which I find unfortunate. I'd always liked that name, thought it was pretty classy. Sort of belied the interior. There wasn't much that you couldn't find there.

Madam

I had a friend once, Claudia, who moved up to the Boston area from New York or New Jersey, someplace where they must be more sophisticated than she – apparently – was. It was late at night. She was tired, overshot the city, and ended up going north on Route 1. Exhausted, she saw a motel, pulled over and went to check in, figuring that she'd find her way to wherever it was that she was supposed to be going in the morning. The name of the motel was the Sir John. (Okay, I know, I know, so she was *really* tired.) The manager was a little surprised that she wanted the room for the whole night, but I guess he figured, what the hell. She didn't notice that the motel was right next door to the Golden Banana, one of the North Shore's biggest and most famous strip clubs. She sure as hell didn't get much sleep that night.

Anyway, Claudia told me once – years later – that while she was sleepily driving back south on Route 1 into the city the next morning, she was looking around her, and figured that there wasn't anything that anybody could possibly want in terms of commodities that they couldn't buy on Route One.

That was how I felt about the After Dark supplement in the *Phoenix*. There wasn't anything that you could possibly want that you couldn't find there.

I thought that After Dark was as wicked as it got.

* * * * * *

My innocence was in part the product of my personality and in part the product of my past. I really do believe at some level that people are fundamentally good and that, given the opportunity, they do the right thing. My observation of and occasional participation in thoughts and actions that are less than pure haven't completely tarnished this fundamental belief.

My experience – well, that's something else altogether. If I went by my experience, I'd probably be as cynical as they come.

I grew up in the South, where ladies are ladies, "sir" and "ma'am" are common, and when people ask you how you are, they wait for an answer. That's a far cry from the brisk how-ya-doin'? of the Northeast. I really do believe that there's a little of Scarlett O'Hara in every white woman who grew up in the South, a fundamental belief that good manners can get you through just about any situation. For a very long time, I expected people to behave well – just because they should.

That was not exactly the best upbringing for my line of work, but I've also found that it tempers the cynicism that is part and parcel of my profession and makes me – or so I'm told – reasonably pleasant to work with. Perhaps not the most overwhelming of compliments, but there are days when I'm willing to settle for reasonably pleasant.

It also means that I smile and acknowledge toll collectors as people, am overwhelmingly polite to telephone operators, and am, of course, kind to dogs and small children. Or is that children and small dogs? I never seem to get that one quite right.

In any case, what the South did give me, besides that take on life and an accent I still cannot entirely get rid of, was a wealth of literature. I love to read; I read everything that is ever been set in front of me, from cereal boxes to VCR instructions, but the voices of the South are what echo the loudest in my world, then and now.

Though proper Southern ladies might blanch at the thought of running an escort service, I haven't really gone overboard after all. For many of these writers are the same ladies who embrace sexuality with gusto and imagination, who write obsessively and far into the night of breaking free from the oppression of white society (and, some of them, of male society), who tell of awakening to a world where they can be managers of their own destinies. I think that, in the end, some of them might even have applauded me.

It was perhaps under their guidance that I made the final decision about my new business – choosing a niche, an area of specialization, if you will. And when I chose it I was completely aware of the ladies' voices telling me that it was the right thing to do.

I decided to focus on guys who wanted more than just sex. I know that may sound odd, coming from a madam; but while sex is the blanket under which we sleep, so to speak, it's not all about sex. Far from it.

It's about power, and it's about loneliness, and it's about a media that constantly tells people that they can Have It All, then springs Real Life on them like some cruel joke. Sex is the battlefield. Sex is the forum where all this stuff gets negotiated, worked out, and practiced. We make so much of sex because we make it mean far more than it was ever supposed to mean. It is only we Americans, with that puritanical past that we can't seem to rid ourselves of, who see sex in terms of its excesses: as everything or as nothing.

So it's not surprising that all of our issues either have to do with, or get worked out via, our sexuality. It's a pity, but it's a reality; and a business that aims to take advantage of Americans' hang-ups does well to note that.

In the end, what I decided to do was provide girls who were educated or on their way to being educated, girls who could talk about politics or literature or current events and keep up with the conversation, girls who could do more than just be blonde. Those were the girls, I thought, who would bring in the clientele that I wanted – middle-class guys who want vanilla sex and a chat.

That's not as crazy as it sounds. It wasn't just that I wanted the distinction of running a literary escort agency, though there's something to be said for that – it evokes images of people reading erotica to each other while getting undressed, which is an image that I have to say I rather like.

No, my decision was completely practical. I wanted those clients, first and foremost, because they are the lowest risk around.

They weren't going to get too weird and hurt somebody. They weren't going to threaten me with exposure because they would mostly be married (or at the very least, in a career of some sort) and in no position to seek exposure themselves. They were going to order up their entertainment like they ordered takeout – and I planned to be their favorite restaurant.

It was a great plan. Has it worked out? More or less.

And therein, I suppose, lies the rest of this tale.

NIGHT ONE CHEZ PEACH

I placed my first ads in the After Dark section of the *Boston Phoenix* and waited with some trepidation for them to come out.

One of the ads was advertising for girls to come work for me ("education required," I had written), and the other was for the service itself. Both had a boudoir-lace edging and stood out, if I do rather smugly say so myself, among all the screaming ads urging readers to "try out my tits" and to "cum all over my ass."

I had already hedged my bets. During my transition between the suburbs and the Bay Village, I had been doing more than just decorating (although I have to say that my new apartment, with its skylights, exposed brick walls, and claw-footed bathtub, had indeed been absorbing quite a lot of my energy). I had also been talking to my former colleagues, asking them if they knew anyone who would like to work for me. That wasn't stealing from Laura, I rationalized. I was employing a network, something altogether different. And of course I got names.

To tell the truth, I don't always run the employment ad these days. Not every week, anyway. Maybe one week out of the month. The reality is that from the beginning I've had the most success getting potential employees through a network – friends, acquaintances, cousins, colleagues, fellow students.

It makes *them* happy, since they are referred by someone who knows how I work, who knows that I won't be weird or dangerous or take advantage of them. It makes *me* happy, too, because referrals aren't very likely to be cops.

So the first Thursday that the *Phoenix* came out with my ad, I was ready. The phone lines were set up: one for clients to call in on, one for my outgoing calls, another as a strictly personal line. I had voice mail, I had call waiting and call forwarding, and, just for security, I had my Yellow Pages. I had my textbooks. I had a stack of mindless magazines, a pen, some scrap paper. I was sitting in the middle of my canopied bed with my television on to keep me from getting too nervous, and I was *ready*.

My voice mail message implied much more than it said. "Hi, we're busy right now, but someone can talk to you if you call us back after five today." I could imagine what the caller might think when he heard those words, filled with a breathy double entendre. He probably was fantasizing that the place was filled with women, maybe having sex with each other while they wait. (That, I have discovered, is a premiere fantasy for most of my clients, the idea that women just can't wait to rip each other's clothes off every chance they get.) I know what callers had assumed when they called Laura's place. Of course, in her case, they were correct – minus the jumping on each other part of it: a lot of beautiful girls, scantily clad, each one sitting patiently, just waiting for that one caller to ask for her. Well, chez Peach, it was a little different. It was just me.

But they didn't have to know that.

I had hoped for some modest business. Maybe a couple of calls on my first night, some contacts for future work. I knew that my voice, with its Southern undertones of peach blossom and bourbon and hot nights, was seductive but businesslike. I knew that anybody who called could easily be enticed to call again. I had some confidence and I expected a nice opening night.

What I got was an avalanche.

This was a step on the learning curve. Clients, I learned, absolutely love new girls, girls they have never seen before, girls who are new to the business. They adore them. I don't know if it's some sort of little sick initiation rite that they're imagining doing, or something leftover from the ever-popular deflowering-the-virgin concept, but whatever it is, they *love* new girls.

Their assumption was that a new agency must be full of them.

I was hard-pressed to handle all my calls that night. Some weren't serious, they were just checking me out, testing the waters, trying to pull me into some erotic chat, but my time at Laura's had taught me how to deflect them – I wasn't going to play their reindeer games. Others were dead serious: who did I have that I could send out to them *right now*? There were the perusers of menus, sitting back comfortably, perhaps with a snifter of brandy to hand, asking me to go through my offerings one course at a time. "Ah, yes, and you said that you might have someone else a little older? Can you tell me about her, too? Okay, now remind me again – the one named Tina …?"

There I was, in the midst of it all, answering phones, putting people on hold, racking my brains to keep names straight and numbers remembered, trying to screen these guys so that I wouldn't send someone out to see a homicidal maniac my first night in business.

The three women I had lined up already were frantically working the telephones, themselves calling up possible recruits.

"Hi, Peach? This is Kara, I'm a friend of Stacey's, she asked me to call you."

I cut right to the chase. "Super. What do you look like?"

Kara, no beginner herself, was clearly used to the drill and rattled her stats off in a practiced manner. "I'm a redhead, shoulder-length hair, I'm twenty-two. C cup bra. I weigh 123 pounds, five-foot-six, and I've got a car."

The last part snagged me right away. "Okay. Can you get over to Newton in half an hour?"

"Sure." She sounded amused.

I riffled through my scribbled notes, most of them in the margins of my textbook. If anyone were ever to read it after me, they'd be in for a shock as the pages were scrawled with my notes … *CARL AT THE FOUR SEASONS, BLONDE …*

I found what I was looking for. "Okay, give this guy a call, Bill Thompson, 555-5454. Call me back after you talk to him, to confirm." I disconnected, then called Bill myself. "I've got this adorable redhead who's dying to see you. She'll give you a call in a minute, and she can be there in half an hour. Her name is Kara. Just give her directions." I hung up before Bill could say anything. This was not the time to chat: I was on a roll.

"Hello? Hi, yes, this is Peach. Where are you located, sir? The Plaza? Can I confirm your name with the reception desk? Great. Do you have any particular preferences? Okay, yes, I do have a stunning blonde, she's a college student, she's 34-24-32 and weighs 110 pounds. Her name is Lacey. I know that you'll like her."

Looking back, I don't know how I got through that night. I don't even remember what was on television (for me, that's an extraordinary statement, because TV is definitely my friend). My magazines and Yellow Pages had been kicked off the bed. The ashtray was overflowing with cigarettes I had lit and then forgotten. I was setting up calls one after the other, stretching out late into the night. "Pam? Honey, can you take another two calls? You're the best, thanks. I have John in Cambridge and Louis at the Four Seasons, in that order. You can call them both now. Here are their numbers. Do you have something to write on?"

Finally, I had to begin telling people they needed to call back the next day. Some took it well; others, not so well. I remember hanging up the phone after one guy called me names at the top of his voice, tiredly massaging the back of my neck, the realization dawning that this was going to work.

It wasn't until three-thirty in the morning that I shut off the phones, padded into the kitchen, opened the bottle of Veuve Cliquot that I had left chilling in the refrigerator, and toasted myself. My new agency – Avanti – lived!

I had suddenly, mysteriously, become a madam.

A HEAD FOR NUMBERS

I don't think that I left my apartment for three days after that.

I was blessed with a great memory for numbers, so I didn't need to develop a routine for keeping information that would leave traces behind: no one will ever break into my place and find a mythical "little black book," because it simply doesn't exist. I found that the memorization skills that had served me well in school were again coming to the fore, and that I could, absurdly, remember nearly all the numbers of the people who had called me that first crazy night.

I probably found the only job in the world where my favorite party trick is a professional asset.

I had hired Jake, a driver, through one of the girls I'd met at Laura's place. It was the girl's brother, actually, who worked for a taxi service by day and picked up whatever jobs he could find in the evenings; she said he spent all his time and money at the Suffolk Downs horse races. Since three of the girls working for me that first night didn't have cars, I'd kept him busy. He stopped by my apartment at the end of the night and dropped off the money the girls had given him to hold for me, my part of what they had earned. Back then, my agency fee was sixty dollars an hour, and I just asked the girls to give the fees to Jake. They paid him out of their own take from the call, usually around $20, depending on the distance he had to drive.

Now I called him and asked him to meet up with the girls who had their own cars and pick up their fees, as well; I wasn't about to leave anyone holding my money for too long. Not this soon in the relationship, anyway.

I sat on my bed and counted my money. Then I counted it again. And again. I had put out eighteen calls that first night, at $60 a call for me. I had calculated what to charge based on what I had learned from Laura – and a few surreptitious calls to some other agencies. Prepared, that's me.

Even better than all that, I had a waiting list for the next couple of days.

There wasn't much time to rest on my laurels, though – the telephone kept ringing. The word was out, apparently, that Avanti was the newest, hottest service in town. Everyone wanted to try me out.

Everyone wanted to work for me. I did quick phone interviews and prayed that the girls I was talking to had given me accurate descriptions of themselves. "Okay, that's super, and what name do you want to use? Zoë? All right. Check in with me when you're ready to go to work and I'll see what we can do for you. Yes; I'm Peach, that's right."

I didn't pick up the client line until I felt I was ready. I had a quick cheat sheet of who was available and what she looked like; then I took a deep breath and plugged in the work line, and we were off and running again.

Jake was elated. "Hot damn, this is the best it's ever been. I've driven for other services and it was nothing like this. Anytime you need a driver, I'm your guy."

I didn't have time for mutual backslapping. "Can you meet Melanie at the Star Market on Commonwealth and pick up some money from her? She's holding $360 for me. She'll be there at six. She's driving a red Subaru."

"Sure thing, Peach."

I yawned and walked into the kitchen to make some coffee. I'm not a big coffee-at-night drinker, but it looked like I was going to need it. Wearing my socks, my sweats, and my favorite Paris Hard Rock Café T-shirt, I probably didn't look like anybody's idea of a madam. Which was perfectly fine with me.

Around midnight, I got a call from Robert, a French guy I'd met at a party I'd gone to while I was still working for Laura. We'd hit it off – though in a strictly platonic sort of way, which I have to say was somewhat to my disappointment – and hung out together fairly often. He'd helped me decorate my apartment, getting so enthusiastic that at one point I wondered if his lack of interest in me, combined with his total devotion to interior design, added up to his being gay. "So how's it going? Raking in the money?"

"Oh, you know," I said, nonchalantly. "Just another so-so day."

I could imagine the grin over the phone line. "Thought I'd stop by and give you a present to congratulate you."

This was good news. Robert was, by profession, a drug dealer, and I had just been feeling sleepy. "I'm here, feel free to drop by."

He arrived just as the phones were slowing down. He had beer, coke, and a friend. "This is Stuart," he said. "Where's your Scrabble board?"

My friend Jenny used to say that I ran an intellectual salon, with bright and interesting people clustering around me. She said what I did was hold court with them, on almost a nightly basis. If she was right – and I do think that she exaggerated things just a little – then those soirées started on my second night of business, with Robert, Stuart, and the

Scrabble game. I waited until my last girl had been called out, then I unplugged the phones, opened a beer, did a line, and we were off.

* * * * * *

I worked out my own system. When a girl arrived at the client's home or hotel room, I'd have her give me a call. She told the client that it was so I'd know that she had arrived safely. ("Peach worries about me, you know.") But in reality I was both starting the clock running, and giving her an option to get out of a situation in which she felt uncomfortable.

It's funny, as I look back on it now. These days, I give Sam secret code words to keep him safe. "The password is Twinkletoes. Don't ever, *ever* go anywhere with anybody, even if that person is a grown-up, even if that person says that I sent them. Do you understand? If they say that I sent them, you ask them for the password. If they don't know it, then run away from them."

So I guess I had already started that same thing with my girls. "If you feel funny about anything, you can get out of there. When you call me, pretend that I just told you your sister called and is sick. You can apologize to the client, tell him to call me back, but that you have to leave. And then get out of there. You can tell me later what was wrong. Trust your instincts."

In fact, I was actually a parent long before I had children: I had my clients and I had my girls. They were all as demanding as any two-year-old – maybe even more so. It goes with the territory.

These are people who are carrying around a lot of baggage. Well, honestly, think about it: you can't live in the margins forever without eventually becoming marginal yourself.

At best, working as a callgirl can be a necessary interim step on your way to someplace else – as long as you keep that "someplace else" firmly in mind. It's the women for whom the work becomes a run-on sentence who have the real problems.

But it *can* be good, believe it or not. It can be a way for a single mother to pay the rent and still spend her days with her children. It can be an abused woman getting the financial independence she needs to get out of a violent life. It can be the final stage of the Ugly Duckling becoming a beautiful swan, and proving it to herself and to the world. However – and this is a big however – those are the best-case scenarios, and they only work if you can manage to use the profession, rather than let the profession use you.

But it's seductive, sometimes too seductive, and it's easy to forget the password, the talisman, the way out.

It's easy to think that this is the Real World.

First off, there's the money. It's been called the highest-paid profession in the world for women: that may not always be true, but in terms of hourly work, it has to be right up there. Certainly from my point of view, there is nowhere else on earth, with my education and my qualifications – or lack thereof – where I could be making the kind of money that I do. And it's the same for the girls that work for me.

So this gets seductive after a while. You look at the other jobs you could have. They're paying less than a tenth of what you're making, and leaving becomes a really difficult decision to make. You have to have something set up, ready to segue into, otherwise you won't make a clean break. People who keep coming back never really leave in the end. The longer they keep at it, the harder that decision will be, and the longer they'll put it off.

Then there are the drugs – there are always the drugs. They're so pervasive in this life that there's almost no way of avoiding them. The names change, the highs change, but the drugs remain.

Wherever you go, it's easier than easy to get drugs. You practically have to fight off people trying to sell them to you. This was truer at the beginning of my career as a madam, though some drug use remains a constant even today.

That was how Robert made his living in those days. He'd get some coke and divide it into lots of little bags, then he'd go hang out in the clubs, selling the stuff. When it's past midnight and people are drunk and have run out of their stash and want to keep going, Robert can pretty much charge whatever he wants – for whatever they want.

There's the whole countercultural thing, too. It's probably the same dynamic that you see in teenagers, the ones who despise anything "normal" and feel themselves to be above all that. They turn pagan or Goth or grunge, and soon their friends are the only ones who understand them and the rest of the world is just oh-so-boring. That same dynamic operates in adults, too. Or maybe just so-called adults.

But after a while, you live most of your life at night, you make a lot of money and you spend a lot of money and people want to hang out with you. Eventually you're going to lose interest in any other kind of life. Owning a house? Having kids? Going to work every day? *Please*. That's for people who aren't as hip and cool as I am.

To my mind, that's the worst of it all. We're not cooler than anyone else; we just think we are. We feed on each other's need to believe that, like vampires, and end up like them, too, exhausted and empty, unable to face the light of dawn.

But when you're in it … while it lasts … oh, man, it's fucking *magic*.

JESSE, JESSE, JESSE …

Of course, if you're anything like me, as soon as one thing in your life starts going well, everything else falls apart.

Work was great. I had opened an escort agency. I had some slow nights after the first mad rush, but work was regular, if not predictable. There were problems, but so far, nothing that I couldn't handle.

And then the one thing that I couldn't handle came along. His name was Jesse.

Jesse had, oddly enough, known me before, during a wild and unlucky trip I took to California while I was still at college myself. I had gone with some friends who were convinced that they could beat the odds in Vegas, which they probably could have done, in retrospect, if they hadn't been caught counting cards the first night out. So much for subtlety. So we took the rest of our money and headed for Palm

Springs instead. We had no idea how ludicrously expensive it would be. We lived out of the car for a few days – there were five of us – and then spent the rest of the summer in a kind of leftover hippie place on Manhattan Beach. That was where I met Jesse.

We had a fling, of course. Every proper Eastern girl who goes to California when she's in college has a fling. Don't ever let anyone tell you otherwise. He was, to my inexperienced eyes, quintessentially Californian, with smooth, tanned skin and dirty blond hair and blue eyes that looked like they were looking straight through you, into your soul, into your secrets. He had gorgeous hands, too, with long, sensitive fingers – what my mother would have called musician's fingers. And he knew how to use them.

Within a day I was spending every night, every day, every moment of time I could manage with Jesse and his sensitive fingers. And tongue. And other body parts. He was intoxicating, more intoxicating than any liquor I had ever tasted. He did things to my body I hadn't dreamed could be done. When he undressed he could have leapt from the cover of a romance novel (not that I ever read them, but Jesse was definitely cover material if I had – and I wasn't immune to *that*).

Then he'd take off my clothes, too, and start moving his tongue all over me. Insistently, like he needed me, like he was restraining himself from devouring me. That was a such a turn-on – women like to feel that there's a storm building somewhere – and his cock would be hard and throbbing against me, but his hands would keep moving all the time, and when he finally pushed himself inside me it was always as though every millimeter of my skin was responding, I had become so achingly aware of and in tune with him. Even the air on my skin felt erotic, charged, electric. He would move enough to build the tension, to build the passion, to make me ache for him to continue, then stop thrusting, and the hands would start again, moving, feeling, caressing; and then he'd begin thrusting again. This went on and on and on, through sweat-soaked afternoons, into sweat-drenched nights, until I finally begged him to let me come.

When I did, he would, too. And then he'd start caressing me all over again.

I'd never known a man who didn't go to sleep, or get up, or do something else irritating after an orgasm. Never. I'd had boyfriends reach for the remote and turn on the game after an orgasm, for heaven's sake (and, in one unfortunate instance, I had one who reached for it before the orgasm; but that was most decidedly the end of him). Not only did Jesse stay there; he started in all over again.

It was every girl's wet dream, and, for that marvelous, magical summer, it was mine.

But summers end. I went back to Emerson college, paid attention to my studies, and Jesse became a memory etched in sunlight.

Until he showed up at my doorstep, five years later.

I fell for him all over again.

* * * * * *

I opened the door and stood there, staring at him, in shock. I had been anticipating the cab driver with my turkey dinner from the Union Oyster House.

So I was thinking about turkey and mashed potatoes and gravy, and then suddenly there was Jesse.

"Hey, baby," he said, a little awkwardly, and then he smiled and the world around us lit up.

"Hi." I couldn't say much more – my breathing was a little ragged at that point. "Jesse."

The smile broadened, and he walked up the three stairs to where I was standing in the doorway, his body tall and hard and tanned, just inches away from mine.

This was definitely not good.

Then he kissed me. And the sunshine and the surf and the happiness of Manhattan Beach sparkled all around us, even on a rainy night in Boston. I put my arms around his neck and hung on for dear life. To his credit, the man carried me into my apartment.

We barely got the door shut behind us before we were tearing at each other's clothes, our breath coming in hot little spurts, his hands suddenly all over me again.

The phone rang.

I froze. Jesse didn't. "Let the machine get it," he murmured in my ear, before gently biting it. "You're going nowhere."

Well, actually, I was. I wrenched myself away from him, flustered. "I have to," I whispered. "I'll be right back."

But of course I wasn't. I ran into my bedroom – where I had all the phones – and immediately got tied up in negotiating with a client who wanted three girls. I couldn't pass on that. So I sat and felt my heartbeat return to normal as I dealt with him, found three appropriate girls I could send, dispatched them, alerted my driver, and put out another call. When at last the dust had settled, I looked up and saw Jesse leaning against the doorjamb.

"Well," I said, with an attempt at humor, "at least I don't have to tell you what I do for a living these days."

He smiled, that slow, crooked, heat-filled smile of his. "No," he agreed. "You don't." He walked across the room and stood beside the bed. Without thinking about what I was doing, my hands – completely of their own free will – unbuckled his belt and unzipped his jeans. As soon as his cock was in my mouth the years disappeared, and all I wanted, all I could think about, was making love with him.

Which we did, with the phone ringing and being answered intermittently, for the next ten hours.

Jesse had brought some wine, and I had a fair store of coke on my dressing table, courtesy of Robert, so sleep was pretty much out of the question. I stopped doing the phones after two in the morning, and I don't remember what happened to the turkey dinner delivery. We stopped touching and moaning and probing and licking only long enough for a sip of wine, tipped from his mouth into mine, or a line of coke, expertly put out on my breast for him to snort, or a trip to the bathroom or refrigerator. I was fascinated; I'd never seen a man do coke and keep an erection. Jesse had amazing talents.

Things are not what they seem, however.

It turned out that Jesse was moving to Boston. He needed a place to stay for a few days. Could he stay with me? Panting in my postcoital exhaustion, of course I said yes. And it was fine, it really was. For a while.

He wasn't looking for a job, not right away, but that didn't matter, because I had more girls needing rides than my regular driver Jake could manage. And what Jesse *did* have was a car. So off he went in the evenings, driving young, beautiful women to obscure destinations and then coming back at one or two in the morning to make love to me for the rest of the night. We'd finally fall asleep toward dawn, and I don't think that I ever woke up before four or five in the afternoon. That was when I was starting to deal with the hangovers, right when the phones started ringing.

Bad for business? You'd think that working with a hangover might be, though in reality I don't think that anybody particularly cared. Both my clients and my employees were too self-centered to notice when I wasn't really on my game.

But I noticed it, and it was a problem for me. Another problem was my nights off, when I'd either get one of the girls I trusted to answer the phones for me or else shut down entirely for the night. Going out became a real problem. Jesse was witty and handsome. He had bought an Armani suit with the proceeds of his driving (though he never seemed to be getting enough together for an apartment of his own), and he loved the clubs, the chicest venues, the new restaurants. I lived off Columbus Avenue, in the center of Boston's trendiest dining scene, and Jesse was at his best there, looking handsome, pronouncing on a wine, savoring a sauce.

All this cost a bundle, of course, and since I was making the money, I invariably paid. But the excitement of being with the best-looking guy in the place starts to pale when you're picking up his tab, night after night after night.

It wasn't just the money, though. It was the girls. Girls who were supposed to be dropped off at a certain time were inexplicably late. Girls whose apartments were on Jesse's way somewhere else. Somehow, I had a sneaking suspicion that I wasn't the only woman in Boston succumbing to his California charms.

He denied it all, of course. He soothed my worries with kisses and champagne and cocaine. I'd sigh, relent, and tell myself that it really was all right – but it wasn't. Waking up with the late-afternoon sun slanting through my blinds, my mouth dry, my head feeling like a sledgehammer had taken up residence inside, and a nose filled with blood-encrusted snot, I was having a whole lot of second thoughts about my judgment.

The trouble was that we never actually talked about anything. Not ever. We *did* things; we fucked; we ate and talked about the business when necessary; but other than that, we never talked. We certainly didn't discuss anything as mundane as when he planned to stop freeloading off me.

I knew that there was disappointment in Jesse, somewhere. I knew he felt that the world wasn't giving him his due, that he deserved more than he was getting, and that I was somehow there in the mix, part of him feeling that he deserved to get something back.

What that was, honestly, I don't know. Certainly Jesse had never made any great contributions to the world that warranted his intense sense of entitlement.

His disappointment made him restless. Even when he was with me, he was always moving – turning on the CD player, turning on the TV, pacing, talking, tapping, complaining, anything to keep from thinking, from dwelling on that narcissistic disappointment.

I still am amazed at how forceful and strong I was with my clients, my drivers, my girls; and yet I lost all that strength and confidence when I was around Jesse. I spent month after month with this man – if you can call our loose liaison being together – and hated myself the entire time for not standing up to him.

When I finally did, I learned another of life's lessons: let someone into your life, and you're handing them the means to hurt you on a silver platter.

And he did.

We had a fight, a dazzling, brilliant fight, with objects hurled and broken and the downstairs tenant pounding angrily on the door. The names Jesse called me were bad enough. The sneering references to my sexual preferences and performances were pretty awful. But the things that he said about me in the clubs, to other people, to people who mattered – I couldn't understand how he could hate me so much to want to destroy me like that. I just didn't get it.

And it was humiliating, embarrassing in a way that I'd never been embarrassed before. I thought about wearing sunglasses all the time. I thought about not going out. I tried not to think about any of it.

So he left, came back, left again, and came back again. My business and my popularity were growing, but here I was emotionally ensnared by a man with the temperament of a spoiled child.

The irony is that I knew what I was doing. I could see it, I didn't like it, and yet I kept doing it.

And the whole time we were together, I can't ever remember Jesse calling me Abby.

That should have said it all.

ESCORT BUSINESS ETIQUETTE

These days, after the school bus leaves, there's peace in my house. Sunlight streams in through the living room windows, music is playing, and for a few minutes I could be the very picture of any stay-at-home mom. I tidy things up, make myself my own special coffee with cream and vanilla, and I think about how to spend my day. In some ways, once Sam leaves for school, my life isn't all that different from what it had been before, back in what I sometimes think of as the Bad Old Days.

Except, of course, for the fact that last night I went to bed immediately after calling out the last girl, whereas in the past that was when the partying just got started. Then there's also the fact that it is now eight o'clock in the morning, a time of day that I didn't see all too often for a whole stretch of years.

The drugs were part of it too, of course. You can't do lines of coke all evening and expect to slide right off into a blissful sleep. But it was more than that; I really did feel that the night, the time after darkness fell, was when I came into my own. I'd stop putting out calls around midnight or one o'clock, and that was when *my* time truly began – or so I thought.

If I was alone I'd sit and write – poetry, mostly, long tangled verses exploring the world as I saw it, trying to answer the questions I was constantly formulating. I had always loved to write, and those long silences after the frenzy of business finally gave me my space, my time.

Often, though – probably three or four nights a week – someone would come by, and after I put the phones to bed we'd party. Wine and coke and Scrabble, the pillars of my nights. Often it was Robert, headed here after the bars closed at two, his leftover sales product in his pockets. He'd usually bring someone, and before long, it seemed, I had a lot of people who were happy to sit and discuss the secrets of the universe after hours *chez moi*.

I never saw it the way that Jenny did, as an intellectual salon; but perhaps it was. She always saw things in me that I never took seriously.

As time went by, the Scrabble board began to disappear, and we mostly talked. On the nights that I had too much Pinot Grigio, my drink of choice, I read aloud the poems and short stories that had filled my predawn hours of solitude, and it became a critique group of sorts. We talked about immigration rules, the impending overpopulation of the planet, and Freud's take on women.

In retrospect, I don't know how coherent we all were. I have a nasty suspicion that I get single-tracked once I've had too much to drink, but, Lord, we had fun.

Once in a great while I'd have become friendly enough with one of the girls who worked for me to invite her over on one of these nights. Usually I'd have her come by after her last call and give me my fee, and then she'd stay for the wine, the coke, and the company. That was how Jen and I became close at the beginning – she'd stop by and stay for Scrabble and conversation.

I didn't do that at first. In fact, I've always had a strong aversion to actually meeting the girls who work for me, but Jenny insisted. After that I occasionally met some of my other women, though I was never comfortable doing that. I made few exceptions to this rule – though now I have several close friends who I met when they worked for Avanti. In general, though, as I said, I've wanted to keep the line firmly drawn between Work and Real Life. Between Peach and Abby. Between fantasy and reality.

I know that at times this has seemed almost comical to people. Someone might be over, we're talking, and I have to take a break to call a girl out or speak to a client. Then I turn back and resume whatever it is we're doing, wherever it is we left off. I don't talk about my work with anybody, because it's just that: work. I don't expect my programmer friends to bring up coding difficulties, and while my line of work may seem sexier and more interesting to a lot of people than writing code, frankly, it isn't to me.

In any case, I rarely meet the girls who work for me. Back then it was because of the distance I wanted to create; these days, it's a matter of temperament, or lack of shared interests, or – well, okay, I'll be honest – age. Most of them are young, in college or just out of it. Most of them haven't been in some of the dark places I've been and haven't the wisdom that comes from having been there.

* * * * * *

As middle age approaches, we all become more concerned about mortgages and healthcare and parenting issues than we are with sexual freedom. I played the game for a long time, but frankly, its discourses, philosophies, and problems simply aren't relevant in my life anymore. I've moved on.

And I know too much to go back.

Also – and I probably only admit this to myself in those dark, predawn moments of honesty – there's another issue at play here. I regularly send girls into places that I myself wouldn't want to go. Uncomfortable places. Degrading places. Bad places. There's a part of me that doesn't feel all that good about that. Meeting them, knowing them, their lives and concerns, joys and personalities – that might make it worse.

That might make it impossible.

I'm not naïve enough to pretend that what I do is the most wholesome job on the planet. Mind you, I try to make it the best that it can be, but at the end of the day, it's prostitution, and there aren't a whole lot of ways to dress that up. If someone's going to go into this line of work anyway, mine is probably the best service to work for, but that doesn't mean it's necessarily the best calling in the world.

I do believe that it makes a tremendous difference, my being a woman. I've heard horror stories about some of the services run by men in this town. Owners who are little more than pimps and help themselves to the services they offer – for free, of course, which lends a whole new meaning to the concept of sexual harassment on the job. There are drivers who take advantage of the girls, sell them drugs, take more than their cut from what the girls earn. Those are services run by men.

There's something inside those men, in the inner recesses of their psyches, that says it's okay to use women, it's normal to use women, it's nothing personal. But they're wrong: it's always personal. These are human beings, not kilos of coke.

They lie to the girls. They don't screen their clients. They make the girls do all the negotiating for what acts will be performed, and at what price. They make them do a minimum number of calls whenever they sign on and force them to go to clients they don't want to see. They tie the girls to them by getting them hooked on drugs, then owing them money. After a while, it just starts feeling hopeless to the girl, like she'll never get out.

I've heard more horror stories than I can even remember. I've learned things I never wanted to know.

* * * * * *

Valerie should have come to me first, but she didn't. She was in her first year at Boston University and her parents had just gotten a divorce, so there was really no place to go home to anymore, and there was a lot less money around, as her parents were spending it tearing each other apart in court. So she decided to earn her own money.

She worked at a bar on Columbus for a while, graduated to an upmarket bar, but injured her ankle and couldn't work the hours. She did data entry at the school, but funding ran out and the job disappeared.

The bills, however, did not.

She looked in the Yellow Pages and picked out a service that was advertising for escorts. She was interviewed over the phone that afternoon and told that a driver would pick her up that night at six.

She was thrilled. The advertisement had a couple of line drawings of slinky women in little black dresses, sipping champagne. This was, she thought, her entrée to Boston's nightlife, all the glitter and excitement that she had felt was passing her by as she confined her own social life to the student union and the coffee shops on Commonwealth Avenue.

So she put on the little black dress and the black lace underwear and the stockings with the seams up the back, and waited, a little breathlessly, for the driver to pick her up.

He wasn't very nice to her, to start with. He gave her the rules: she had to negotiate separately for anything that the client wanted, and she'd better get at least $60 for a blow job, and get it in her hand before each agreed-upon act. She had to give all of the money to the driver when she left the client's house; the driver would give her her share, himself. Oh, and she'd better be fast, because he wasn't supposed to wait for anyone for more than a half hour.

This is the way it's supposed to be, thought Valerie, and agreed. But it turned out that they didn't have any immediate destination, and as they waited for the driver's beeper to go off, he offered her a nip from his flask, a snort from his stash. When she refused, he told her it was required. When she refused a second time, he raped her.

"Who was I going to complain to?" Valerie asked me, her voice forlorn. "I had a black eye from struggling with him, and he threw me out of the car. He said no guy would want to see me all beaten up like that. Where was I supposed to go? To the police? They'd laugh. Women who put themselves in situations like that get what they deserve, that's what they'd say."

So much for the glitter of the nightlife. When she came to me – she liked the ad that said I was looking for women with education – I tried to send her only to my nicest clients, the really good guys, but there weren't that many of them, and I knew she was working for another service as well. After a while, she stopped checking in. A few months later she called and asked for work, and I sent her to Jimmy Pearlstein, a nice guy over in Brookline who I knew would treat her well. She didn't stay for the whole hour, and he wasn't too happy with me when he called me back. "Shit, Peach, she looked like hell, and she kept asking for a tip. What's with this tip thing?"

After that, I never heard from her again, and I tried never to think of her. If I let myself go there, I'd see a whole gallery of them, frightened voices, pale faces, the women who passed through my agency and disappeared.

Some of them didn't, I'm pretty sure, go on to bigger and better things.

I've talked about this before, and I can't say it enough. The women who make it are the ones with a plan. The ones who see working as an escort as a step on a journey that has a selected ultimate destination. The ones who have a real life somewhere else, with real dreams and plans. Those are the ones who stay healthy, who move on, who follow other dreams.

But the ones who start seeing the work as a long, never-ending path, a run-on sentence, those are the ones who drop through the cracks. Those are the ones who could really haunt me if I allowed them to.

I've had people I'm proud to have worked with. One woman went on to open her own theater company in Seattle. Another got a teaching certificate and is now at an elite private school in Virginia. Yet another is doing someone's taxes for a whole lot of money in Manhattan. Jenny had written novels before, and working for me enabled her to realize her dream of doing it full-time.

I like seeing that: I like thinking that I was some sort of way station for them on their way to somewhere else, that what I did didn't just not hurt them, but helped them.

They help me keep the nightmares at bay.

If I didn't have women like them, I couldn't keep doing this job, not even for the money. And I won't kid you – if there's a lot of money in being an escort, there's even more in being a madam.

But being a madam – especially one with ethics, which is how I like to see myself – well, that's tricky. Like picking your way through a bog at midnight, and there's never a right answer.

There's no etiquette guide to being a madam. The job doesn't come with an instruction manual. Sometimes you just have to cross your fingers and hope that you're doing the right thing, because, man, you never know for sure.

* * * * * *

But back to the differences between Avanti and the other services in Boston. Am I trying too hard to justify what I'm doing? I think not; I'm trying to be the best tour guide that I can.

I think there's some sort of leftover pimp mentality that infects men when they run a business like this one. They have no idea, not really, what they're asking women to do out there: I do.

I do, and that makes all the difference.

I know what all this feels like, and I really have sympathy and empathy for the girls. I try to be honest about who I'm sending someone to. I try and tell her at the beginning what the client is likely to want from her, and be there for her to vent to afterward if it's necessary. I tell her when someone is obnoxious, or has poor hygiene, or will not be nice to her. I can't picture any of these guys who run services offering their shoulder for the girl to cry on.

And I know that I get a whole different clientele just because I'm a woman, and I think my girls get treated differently because I'm a woman, too. When a guy talks to another guy about sex, there's this inherent frat-sleaze connection between them, and that is sure to translate into how the client sees the girl.

But I'm everything to my clients: confessor, mother, sister. I am the one who promises them escape, delight, pleasure, who extols their manhood, who respects their privacy, who finds whatever they want to be normal and acceptable. In so doing, I am the unattainable Eros that they all long to meet and make love to, and because they can't, at some level they make love to me through my girls.

I didn't learn all of this at once, of course. It was a slow realization, this understanding of the relationship that I form with my clients. I've lost a few along the way because I made mistakes, but as I am writing this, almost all of my business is composed of regulars, guys who have been calling me for years.

So I must be doing something right.

THE BELLE OF BOSTON

Jesse and I didn't really break up – not so that you'd notice. We wouldn't see each other for weeks at a time, and then he'd be back again, acting as if nothing had ever happened.

I should have shut the door in his face.

I should have done a lot of things, I suppose, but I didn't do any of them. I let him in, again and again, over and over, and never questioned the sinking feeling that accompanied his arrival. I was always too glad to see him, grasping at the illusion that there was something real and good between us. Even after that illusion died, my need for it kept its ghost alive, haunting my nights and stressing my days. I thought that I couldn't have an emotional life apart from Jesse, and that's always a recipe for disaster.

It was a sort of drifting existence: he'd drift in and out at will, and I'd wait for him to make the decisions about how and when to reappear. Passive. Helpless. Unconscious.

My social life wasn't doing too badly by then, and frankly, that made my tolerance of Jesse more baffling. I had slowly started to become someone, and I was liking it quite a lot. Robert took me with him to clubs and I got to know the right people, got placed on the right lists, and before long there wasn't anything important on the social scene to which I wasn't being invited.

My clients were amazing, too. You have to remember, I talked with these guys on the phone, night after night. Sure, they wanted to see girls, but at the same time a relationship was being forged between them and me.

We talked about all sorts of things – their work, my work, what I was reading. When all else failed we could always fall back on bemoaning the current crop of Red Sox basketball team players and the promise of victory that was always just beyond our grasp. (They finally made it, of course, in 2004, and my business was *never* as bad as it was during the post-season!) When you talk with someone that much, that often, you start to get close, even if in the most superficial of ways.

I lied to them and they lied to me; but in some cases real truths were told, real vulnerabilities exposed, and something unique and unexpected happened, the sort of thing that only happens after midnight when you're both tired, your nerves are frayed, and you need someone – anyone – to be there for you.

Then there were the ones who were just plain fun. There was a restaurant in those days attached to one of the hotels downtown – very chic, very expensive, some sort of fusion cuisine – that catered to a select group of out-of-town visitors. The owners used to call me to have girls meet the clients at the restaurant, have a meal together, and then go up to the hotel rooms after dinner.

Whenever I went to that restaurant, I felt like a celebrity. I was treated like royalty. I was their guest for the evening. It was really nothing more than the standard quid pro quo that happens in any business, but this was one that gave me an entrée into ever-spiraling levels of social interaction that I'd never have dreamed of attaining on my own.

Then there were the private parties, so many of them: big loft apartments on the waterfront filled with fine art and smoke and muted conversations, lines of cocaine laid out on marble tabletops and sucked up through hundred-dollar-bill straws, outrageous revealing dresses on the women and Armani casual on the men. I was meeting writers, politicians, creative people, powerful people, and all the while some little voice inside me was squeaking about how scintillating it all was, and about how cool *I* was.

Those were the parties that we all went to in those days, plus gallery openings and private shows, and I found myself – somewhat to my surprise, although I can imagine how disingenuous this must seem to you now – at the center of the most animated conversations, the recipient of even more invitations, offers, gifts.

Out in the suburbs, working for Laura, I hadn't realized just how positively my profession was perceived in other places. The suburbs of America are as white-bread, status quo, sexist, racist, and narrow-minded in their own way as any group of religious fanatics has ever been. Not that the world of drugs and Armani suits is socialist; it's just more determined to be diverse, open-minded, and quirky.

Here in the city I was seen as a woman of substance, a woman of power. I suppose that was when I really started seeing myself that way as well.

Then there were the adventures, the countless, ongoing, gossiped-about sexual liaisons and events! Even apart from my work, my world, it seemed, was permeated with sexuality.

I wasn't beyond succumbing myself. I met strangers with dark eyes in smoky bars and ended up sliding my hands into the waistband of their trousers in narrow passageways leading to restrooms or kitchens. I leaned my head on a shoulder at a party and found myself half undressed in a taxi on my way someplace

I had never been before, kissing someone whose name I couldn't for the life of me recall. And I woke up on more than one occasion, my head pounding with a hangover, focusing blearily on the body next to me in the bed, wondering who he was and how he had come to be there.

I went to parties, parties that played fast and loose with intimacy and ended up in the late mornings with naked bodies and haggard faces. I started to read erotica – Anaïs Nin and Henry James and Anne Rice and my personal favorite, Anonymous. The French writers from the turn of the century, drinking absinthe and smoking hashish, dining in restaurants that had heavy embroidered privacy curtains – I loved those books. An era where sex could be bawdy and still retain its mystique, where elegance and outrageous liaisons went hand in hand. I sighed over those books, I really did.

Since I was acquiring a reputation, it was suddenly important to me to act the part. Whereas once I might have dallied with someone young and good-looking, I also realized that who I slept with affected people's perceptions of me, a little like my mother's admonitions, except in reverse. Back then, it was, Don't sleep with anyone, what will people say? Nowadays it was, Sleep with the right people, otherwise what will people say?

A slight shift in perception, nothing more.

This shift had a lot more to do with *not* sleeping with certain people than it did with actually augmenting my list of sexual liaisons. In other words, I didn't go out and decide to sleep with one person or another because it was the chic thing to do. Hell, I can barely wear clothes that someone else dictates is the chic thing to do, much less have fashion dictate anything else in my life. *Au contraire*, I like to think that I may have been the trendsetter in such matters.

In the past, I'd used the excuse of too much partying to not really mind who I woke up with the next morning. Now I suddenly realized that this was like eating fast food: initially satisfying, but not really good for you. And if people know you eat fast food, they're not going to ask your opinion about a gourmet meal. If you're going to be a respected chef, you don't eat at McDonald's.

I wanted to be respected in my line of work, so I started trying very hard to actually decide who I was going to sleep with before I actually did it.

Not a bad policy for anyone, I think.

Jesse was there all the time, too, on the periphery, coming back to me when it suited him. I tried to ignore him, and, when that didn't work, I obsessed instead. I stood around the corner from the apartment he had finally rented over in Bay Village, lurking, lighting cigarettes and putting them out again, watching to see who he went home with, who he woke up with.

The pain of seeing him with someone else was as titillating as it was hurtful. While my heart seemed to turn over inside my chest, my nipples hardened and there was a warmth spreading in my jeans that I couldn't seem to get by any other means.

The reality was that my life, everything I did or didn't do, was under Jesse's influence. I couldn't eat something without wondering whether it was something he would like. I couldn't finally go to sleep in the mornings without wishing that he were with me, and having wretched painful needy thoughts about where he might be.

I couldn't see a movie without wanting to discuss it with him, and this in glaring defiance of the fact that we had never ever discussed anything at all during our time together. I couldn't do anything, say anything, think anything, without immediately relating it to Jesse in some way.

I wasn't totally alive when he wasn't there. I was in a sort of stasis where one goes through the motions, unable to see any part of my life except through the prism of how Jesse would see it. I was marking time until the next telephone call, the next encounter, the next time he would be part of who I am so that I could really feel alive.

He had gotten a beeper by then – God knows why he thought he needed it, though I can make a pretty educated guess – and I can remember with a sort of deep despairing shame the nights, too countless to quantify, when I punched his beeper number into my telephone keypad, over and over and over again. Expecting him to answer. Growing wretched, restless, and upset when he did not. It was a charade, and it was a charade that took a tremendous toll on me.

When he finally came around, I turned into an accusing harridan, a bitch from hell, hardly someone with whom anyone, especially Jesse, would want to spend time. Someone I myself didn't recognize.

When I saw him, it was just so that I could hurl accusations at him. "Where have you been? Why didn't you answer my calls?"

"Baby, I'm busy."

"Why are you doing this to me?" I wailed.

He looked into my eyes. "You're doing it to yourself," he said.

I was too angered by the truth of it, in too much pain by the sting of it, to be reasonable. "You hate me!" I cried. "After everything I've done for you."

He looked at me with something that might have been pity in another person. "Look what you're doing to yourself," he said curtly. "Look at who you're turning into." He closed the door quietly behind him.

Just in time for the vase I had thrown to shatter against it.

When I wasn't thinking about Jesse, I was thinking about myself. I'll be the first to admit it: in the beginning of owning my business, I was about as self-absorbed as they come. I'd call out the last girl for the night and, more often than not, pour a glass of Pinot Grigio and do a couple of lines of cocaine, even if no one was coming over, thinking I was pretty pleased with myself. It made Jesse's unreasonableness even more inexplicable. I was an outlaw, under the radar, doing this thrilling, sophisticated, and illegal thing, and doing it well.

Of course, there was the down side to being the coolest thing around. Waking up in the mornings (or, indeed, in the afternoons) was getting harder and harder, but I shrugged that off as a necessary component of my very exciting life. I don't think that I saw noon for months at a time. No matter: that was what we cool people did.

There was only one window in my bedroom, and it was covered – permanently – with a thick velvet drape, elegant and giving the feeling that one was inside a cocoon. I entertained in my living room, held my salon, laughed and smoked and ate, got high and read, but it was in my bedroom that I worked, with my books and magazines and television, sitting on my brass double bed surrounded by my music and my comforts, ignoring the world into which I sent my girls.

It was never ever daytime in my bedroom.

CALLGIRL SALON

That September a woman called and asked about working for me. She'd left a couple of messages in the daytime – as if I would ever pick up the phone in the daytime! – and I finally talked to her. She sounded cultured and both anxious and amused, a combination I found fascinating. She was older than most of my employees; she said that she was teaching somewhere and only wanted part-time hours. I offered to send her out right away, but she demurred, insisting on meeting me first.

"Sure, right, okay," I said, carelessly, and made a date for lunch, which I then promptly forgot about. I partied after work that night and the next, and on the third day she called again. "I waited for you. Did I misunderstand our appointment?"

Shit. Okay. "No, no, you won't believe this, but I sprained my ankle," I said, glibly. "Let's try for tomorrow."

There was that trace of amusement in her voice again. "Okay, I'll be there." As if she knew already that I wasn't going to be. "Third time's the charm," I promised when she called the following afternoon, and it did look as though I was going to have to see her, if only to get her to leave me alone. She clearly was not planning on going away anytime soon.

We met at Legal's, but went outside to talk. She was pretty – not the standard twenty-something gorgeous, like some of my girls, but beautiful in a refined, European way. When she smiled, her face lit up. She had studied overseas, spoke a number of different languages, talked about Descartes – for God's sake, here she is interviewing to be a callgirl, and she's talking about philosophy! I was entranced.

More importantly, I already had a niche for her. She decided on a work name – Tia – and I sent her that night to my nicest and easiest client. I didn't tell her for three years how much she had intimidated me that first day.

To tell the truth, when I met Jenny, all I could think was that it could have been me, there, with the academic degrees, wearing culture like a sweater draped carelessly around her shoulders. I might have gone that route myself, and I was looking at who I might have become if I had. Sort of a doppelgänger effect.

She was smart and elegant and writing a novel at the time, trying to get out of teaching and make enough money to undo the financial damage some asshole boyfriend had done. That was a little too close to home for me; I didn't talk about it much, but we did talk about other things. She became one of my first really close women friends. Somehow, she brought out the best in me. She listened to my poetry – I used to call her up in the middle of the night, waking her sometimes to read to her; and she listened, not like everybody else did, in order to move on, but she really listened. When I was with Jen I wanted to be better, to be smarter, to stretch myself. I started looking askance at the tabloids and celebrity magazines that surrounded me, and I began rereading some of the classics that I had put aside when I decided that I needed fluff to insulate me from too much thinking.

Eudora Welty writes somewhere about the importance of places – that there are places that become second homes, spiritual homes, which are more real than our actual ones. I wonder if you can extrapolate her sense of space into people. If so, Jenny became, and was for a certain period of time, a spiritual home for me. I mean that intellectually, but also, oddly enough, in a sort of religious sense as well. She was Catholic and talked frequently about her connection to her church, its liturgy, its spirituality. And when she did I found awakening in myself a desire to recover my own Lutheran roots. If it did so much for her, maybe there was something there that I had missed.

She had published novels in the past and had just started thinking about another when we met. That taught me something, too: watching her set a goal, work for it, and achieve it, even though it took years; watching that book go from an idea that she tossed around at my after-work soirées, fueled by the French red wine she insisted on drinking and the lines that we did as she talked about it and worked out scenarios. Years later, *The Illusionist* was published, and I can still read passages from it and remember the same words first being spoken in my apartment in the Bay Village.

She did well with the clients because she attracted guys who were smart and classy, the kind of guys I wanted using my service. She had a couple of regulars, one of whom even bought bottles of her favorite wine to keep on hand for her visits. I was only mildly shocked when I discovered that the wine went for $150 a bottle. She made guys feel that a little bit of class had touched their lives.

Of course, not all of the clients wanted that, and as the months passed I started sensing a little wariness in her, a certain feeling that her days as an escort were numbered. She was the kind of girl who survives the life, precisely because it is not *her* life, and after the first year together I felt her pulling away gradually but firmly. It took her another year and a half to finally give it up; but I think that I knew she was leaving long before she herself did.

She still sparkled at my soirées. It was Jenny who christened them my "salon," who looked at the people I gathered around me and drew parallels from history in the most flattering way.

She thought I was brilliant, so I felt brilliant.

She'd be sweet and passive and go along with whatever I wanted to do in the afternoons, but at other times she'd refuse my suggestion of a movie and take me to the Isabella Stewart Gardner Museum or the Museum of Fine Arts instead. We started working on the outline of a novel we might write together.

We've had our ups and downs over the years; but she is the one friend I have had who has consistently made me feel that I, too, can achieve excellence.

I still go out to Walden Pond, in Concord, these days. Actually, Sam nearly grew up there, sitting on the small beaches and venturing into the sun-warmed water in the hot days of July and August, when the air shimmers with heat and the hawks circle lazily overhead.

Concord and Walden Pond are filled with bright and current delights and memories for me; but in the layers beneath them I remember the days when Jen still worked for me and we'd drive out here in the afternoons – some of them cold and snowy – to do the circuit of the pond, tramping resolutely on the path, our breath visible in the still air around us, me insisting that we stop halfway across so that I could light a cigarette.

Then lunch in Concord afterward, the requisite trip to the Cheese Shop for wine and cheese and vanilla beans, the metal sculpture I bought at the Artful Design, another stop for used books at Barrow's and new ones at the Concord Bookstore, and Snow Pharmacy for the odd ointment called Bag Balm that soothed everything from chapped lips and hands to coke noses. And the freedom of it all; I didn't have a cell phone in those days, so we were alone in an enchanted world, far away from Boston, demanding clients, and ringing telephones.

Every time I come to Concord, she's here, too.

Jen encouraged me to get involved with the Design Group, an arts association in Boston where I volunteered from time to time, dressing up in suits and high heels and talking to potential donors on the phone or showing them around the gallery. She wasn't thinking that it would enrich my future prospects, either. She was one of the few people who didn't fawn over who I was or ask me what I planned to do in the future, as though I were going to grow up and get a real job later on. She didn't ask, When are you going to get serious? What do you want to be when you grow up?

Honestly, the answer would still be the same now as it was then: I want to own my own business. I want to be a madam.

UNDER ... AND
OVER ... JESSE

I was writing poetry again, but an alarming amount of it was focusing on Jesse. I was still stalking him, still morbidly interested in his every move. I ran into him once in a while at one of the regular parties we were all going to and, after one memorable evening when we both got drunk and maudlin at a loft somewhere by the Channel, I even brought him home with me.

I realized that it was a mistake as soon as we reeled in the front door of the apartment. Jesse groped his way with some familiarity to find one of the table lamps and turned it on, and his shadow was immediately cast, grotesque and menacing, on the wall behind him. I flinched, the gesture automatic, and I found myself wondering how my body could be so in tune with what was good and bad for me, while my mind lagged so far behind. Did I really imagine that Jesse would suddenly become someone who he clearly was not? I was more in love with the thought of Jesse than I ever could be with his reality, and my body knew it, but my brain was doggedly assuring me that I could get him back, that I would never love anyone like that again, that he was worth all the problems he caused. Silly brain.

Still, it kept me going there for a while; we didn't even make it to the bedroom. He was pulling at my dress as I stumbled into the small kitchen. (My apartment was designed for people like me, who consider coffee brewing and dinner reheating the major uses for a kitchen.) He grabbed me and forced me up against the sink. I gasped and put my arms around him and started kissing him, deep, demanding kisses, while he fumbled to get my panties off. This accomplished, he lifted me up so that my bare ass was sitting on the edge of the sink; I locked my legs around him while he released my breasts from the bra and sucked on my nipples, holding one breast in each hand. I thought I was never going to be able to breathe again.

Jesse had pulled his turtleneck over his head and had already kicked off his shoes; he grabbed me then and threw me, firefighter-style, over his shoulder and carried me into the bedroom. Court (named for "Court and Spark," my favorite Joni Mitchell song; there had once been a Spark, too, but he had died and Siddhartha had taken his place) gave a loud protesting yowl as I was deposited on top of him, with Jesse pretty much on top of me. He felt heavy and dominating, and I forgot that I was angry with him. I forgot everything but his body on top of mine, his hands grasping my wrists and pinning them to the bed, his rough kisses.

I squirmed out of my dress and bra and by the time I'd finished he was naked, too. He grabbed me and turned me around, so that I was lying flat on the bed on my stomach, and he was all over my back, kissing, caressing, nipping, while still holding me down. I was gasping for breath.

He grasped my hips and pulled me to him, so that he could enter me from behind, and as his cock entered me it felt as though he had plunged it all the way up to my throat. I'd never felt so impaled before. I screamed, and then his hands were on my ass, squeezing and kneading them, finally slapping them, which I found more erotic than I ever had before.

I know that I was screaming by now. He was ramming himself inside me, pausing from time to time to pull his cock almost all the way out, almost, so that I was gasping with need and desire and emptiness, and then he thrust again, harder, deeper, until I could feel him on my cervix and felt that he was inside all of me. And again. Each thrust was harder, more demanding; and when he withdrew, it was to slap my buttocks, again and again and again …

I don't know how long it lasted. I may even have blacked out at some point. There was nothing in the world but us – Jesse and his hard, ramming cock and me with my wet pussy. My buttocks felt hot from the slapping and the kneading, almost enflamed, and the fire seemed to lick up around my whole body. I felt the orgasm coming, building from the front, from my clitoris, to the rear, so that when I came it felt like every organ of my body was quivering.

He slammed into me a final time, reaching forward and grabbing my hair to pull my head up next to his. "Take it," he growled. "Take it, take it, take it … uhhh …"

When he released me I rolled over on my side and remembered how to breathe again.

We lay there together in silence, both of us catching our breath, both of us drenched in sweat. I waited until my heart wasn't pounding quite so painfully and until I was starting to feel a little chilled as the sweat dried on my body.

I realized, with a start, that I wasn't drunk anymore.

I groped on the night table for my cigarettes and pulled one out of the pack. The lava lamp over by the divan gave just enough light for me to find the lighter, flick it, inhale, and look over toward Jesse. He was on his back, arm flung across his forehead, staring at the ceiling. I lay back on my pillow and exhaled smoke slowly toward the ceiling, the relief of it filling my lungs with the sharp little mental push that it always seemed to give me, the sense of well-being.

I didn't say anything, just lay there, waiting for – well, I'm not sure what I was waiting for, actually. And then it happened.

I realized that I didn't want him there.

It came to me sharply and suddenly, the absolute and sure knowledge that this man didn't belong in my bed. Or anywhere else near me, either. That he had no right to just stride back in as though he belonged, as though his place there was permanent and assumed and accepted. That he didn't belong with me anymore than I belonged with him.

I cleared my throat to say as much when the phone rang. The work phone. I sat up, suddenly wanting to not be naked next to him, pulling my silk Victoria's Secret robe around me hurriedly as I answered the call. "Peach? It's me, Evvy."

Part of my brain clicked into work mode. Evvy was on her way to see some guy out in Worcester – nearly fifty miles away. Amazing what kind of time and mileage some people will pay for, and aren't there escort services in Worcester, too? Apparently not, which was fine with me. "What's wrong?" I asked.

There was a bit of a cough, and then, "I can't go, Peach. I just got my period."

Well, that did take care of that, didn't it? I had a couple fetishists among my clientele who would have welcomed the announcement, but the guy in Worcester wasn't one of them. I sighed. "Okay, honey."

Behind me, Jesse turned on the TV. Someone was saying, "We're available twenty-four hours a day, so call now …"

I focused back on Evvy, who was still talking. "I'm really sorry, Peach. It's early, I didn't expect –"

I interrupted her. "It's okay. Go home. Give me a call when you're around again." Being around was my euphemism for being available to work.

"Thanks, Peach. Sorry. Do you want me to call him?"

I hesitated. Normally I'd be the one to make the call, after seeing who else I might be able to get out to him that night. But maybe I had something more important going on here. "Sure, why don't you? Just tell him the truth. He may want to reschedule with you. Otherwise, tell him to call me."

Disconnecting, I turned in the bed to look at Jesse again. He was still naked, sitting on the other edge of the bed, watching the TV screen. I could see, now, that it was an infomercial for astrologers or mediums, something like that. There was a toll-free number flashing at the bottom of the screen.

Hardly captivating, but he seemed entranced. I cleared my throat. "Jesse, it's time for you to go."

"What's that, babe?" He sounded distracted, and I leaned forward, only then realizing that he wasn't looking at the TV at all, but rather scrolling through the numbers on his beeper. Seeing who was important to get back to, now that my five minutes was finished. I felt my stomach clench in the familiar titillation-and-pain combination, and then resolve took over.

Well, nothing like a kick in the pants to help you move along with your decision.

I said, loudly, "I want you to leave now."

That got through to him, all right. "What?" His voice was incredulous – as well it might be, since past experience had been quite the opposite of what was happening now. Usually, I thought bitterly, I spent postcoital time begging him to stay, clutching at him, whining and crying. No wonder he seemed disconcerted. "I want you to go."

He turned to look at me. In the purple light from the lava lamp, and backlit by the TV, he looked suddenly old, dissipated, empty.

I wondered why I hadn't noticed that before.

I got up, pulling the silk robe more closely around me, feeling chilled as if from a breeze or a bad memory. But there was no breeze. I put out my cigarette and faced him, standing and clothed, which had to give me some sort of advantage. His penis was shriveled and small and ridiculous, and I suddenly, irreverently, wondered what I had ever seen in it – or him. There was a drop of semen on his thigh. It was oddly disgusting. "Please leave, Jesse."

He still couldn't quite believe what he was hearing. "It's okay," he said, easily, his tone becoming seductive. "I can stay the night." He lowered his voice still more. "I know you want me to, *cara*."

That fake Italian lover thing was the last straw. I moved to the bedroom door and opened it. "Now," I said firmly.

He stood up, looking even more ridiculous, looking even older. "Fine," he said, the anger and frustration that were always simmering just below the surface of his personality bubbling up. How quickly he could turn from seduction to disdain. "Fine, but you'll be sorry. I don't know when I'll be back." Threats, the fallback position. He reached for his shirt, buttoned it in haste. Unevenly.

"I don't want you to ever come back," I heard myself saying. Wow. I could hardly believe it myself. I felt like applauding.

That got a reaction. "Fuck you," he said intensely. He looked more absurd than ever, standing there in his badly buttoned shirt, his arms thrust into a sweater as he started to dress, with the small and now insignificant penis dangling uselessly below the shirttails.

Against my own better judgment, I giggled. I couldn't help it. They're so proud of those things, men are, but honestly, it looked so ridiculous. It was hard to imagine it ever being connected to passion in any way.

The giggle went over well. Jesse pulled the sweater on, thrust his legs into his jeans, jammed his feet into shoes. A week later, I would find the socks he hadn't bothered to put on tucked under the bed, one of my cats sleeping happily on them. He was too busy working on the grand exit line to bother about something as superfluous as socks. "Fine, if that's what you want." There was menace in his voice now. "But don't go crying for me later. *I won't be there.*"

I didn't say anything, as he glared at me, stomping by with much fanfare, taking care to slam the apartment door so hard that my two downstairs neighbors undoubtedly stirred in their sleep.

I opened the freezer and pulled out the bottle of vodka I kept there. I poured a shot, drank it in one swallow, and then did it again. I switched off the TV and got back into bed, too tired to change the sheets as I thought I probably should. I was suddenly tired, exhausted even, as though the full weight of the relationship, such as it was, had come crashing down on my shoulders.

There was a soft mew, and Court landed next to me. He started purring immediately, kneading my upper arm, delighted to be alone with me again. And as I slipped into sleep that was what I heard, the sound of my cat's contentment – and a little bit of my own.

I'd like to say that it ended there. I'd like to write that I was strong, liberated, able to move on without a backward glance. But life is never that neat, is it? Relationships end raggedly rather than dramatically, in squalor rather than in triumph. Even by the next day I was questioning the wisdom of the stand I had taken.

Jesse may have left, I found, but he cast a long shadow behind him. The worst, the absolute bloody worst, was how I felt after he left. How much I missed him, his warmth next to me, the bed seeming forbidding and empty without him. His bourbon on the sideboard, his T-shirts in the laundry, his hot breath a memory across my cheeks. I missed him more than I could bear. I hated him, I hated myself, but I missed him all the same.

Yet I wasn't going back. Even if I could have faced myself, I couldn't face him. So I did what I never before could have imagined doing.

I left everything. My business. My friends. My life. I stood in my bedroom and felt the walls closing in, like I was suffocating, felt like I was dying. And if that was what was happening, I sure wasn't going to do it here, where Jesse could gloat, where someone, if only my cats, would mourn.

I got on a bus heading to Atlantic City and cried all the way there. Look on a map: Massachusetts to New Jersey – that's one hell of a crying fit.

I'm not even entirely sure what it was I was crying about.

By the time I arrived in Atlantic City, I was exhausted. I stumbled off the bus and I checked into a room at the Sands Casino. The sparkling chandeliers and a sudden cry of delight from one of the blackjack tables that I passed, the ever-present underlying vibration, made up of hope and cynicism and desperation, all surrounded me, wrapping me in a blanket of unreality.

Everybody else was in town counting cards; I was in a bleak hotel room counting pills.

Enough, I thought – but maybe not enough.

I'd brought an eightball of coke with me, too, and I figured that maybe the combination might do it. An eightball – three and a half grams – might even be enough, by itself. So I put on the Do Not Disturb sign and opened the wine (I'd bought screw caps, perhaps not the best vintage, or indeed any vintage at all, but a lot more accessible than fiddling with corks and openers) and started laying out lines on the desktop. I bought some pay-per-view movies and watched them without seeing anything, with my heart hammering in my chest because of the cocaine, my thoughts racing aimlessly in circles.

I started stacking the pills, riffling through them like people riffle through poker chips, feeling their weight and their meaning slipping through my fingers. I lined them up and counted them, then messed them up, did another line, and stacked them instead. I was mesmerized by those pills.

Oddly enough, I didn't like the thought of taking them, though I very much liked what they were promising me. Oblivion. Darkness. Silence. Sleep.

I touched them, caressed them, as though there were some dark meaning that could convey itself to me through my fingertips. The answers to all of life's problems. No more thought, no more dilemmas, no more pain. The question isn't why people kill themselves; it's why people don't. I touched my pills and felt a wave of peace. I was in control. Here, at least – here, *at last* – I was in control. I could make a life-or-death decision.

I riffled through the pills again and slowly the feeling ebbed, the surge of energy drained out of me. I counted them, rotely, and then counted them again. I even brought one to my lips and pressed it against them, but didn't open my mouth.

There was something dark sitting inside me. I didn't know what it was and I didn't know how to make it go away.

I put them all back in their plastic container and leaned back, closing my eyes, holding it close to me. I was in that hallway again, the hallway of the house on South Battery Street, the long streak of light from the window at the end catching the motes of dust hanging all around me, still, as though suspended in air, as though suspended in time.

My father's voice startled me. "Where's Abby?"

A murmur of other voices, then a sound of someone shushing them. "You need all your strength to try and get better." I think that was one of the men who always seemed to be around, one of my father's business associates.

My father's voice again, impatient. "I want to see my little girl."

My back was pressed hard up against the damask wallpaper of the hallway. There was a Chinese vase on the table next to me. I tried to open my eyes, but I couldn't.

"It's best if you rest, Edgar." My mother's voice was clear as a bell through the heavy bedroom door.

It was then that the door opened, slowly, too slowly, and they all came out. The doctor stopped to talk to me for a moment, but I wouldn't talk to them. They weren't going to let me see my father.

I had always assumed that it was he who had not wished to see me; that they were respecting his wishes. The next time I saw him, he was white and lifeless, lying in his Sunday best in a satin-lined coffin. I clutched the pills to me, tears coursing down my face, my knees drawn up to my chest. "Daddy," I whispered. "Daddy, Daddy, Daddy …"

He had wanted to see me. He had asked to see me. I had never known.

I lay there for what seemed like an eternity, feeling warm, dizzy, and exhausted.

Then I put the pills back into my suitcase, pulled out a book, and wandered unsteadily into the bathroom.

I'd brought along a book to read on the bus, which I hadn't touched because I was too busy looking out through the rain-streaked windows and feeling sorry for myself. I'd tossed it into the suitcase and now I picked it up, reading entirely at random. Or was it random? The author was a Southern gentleman, like my father. I sat on the toilet seat and, the tears still drying on my cheeks, started reading; the author immediately drew me in with his descriptions of place; his words were my father's words, the voice of the South.

I sat in that sad casino hotel bathroom and could suddenly, vividly, smell the marshes of South Carolina, as though I were there. A crane hooting. The sticky sweet summer air. I felt a longing – for them, for travel, for home, for anything but feeling sorry for myself, especially over someone as unremarkable as Jesse.

I fell asleep sometime after that, dreaming of warmth and azaleas and the sweat of Southern summers, and when I woke up it was sometime the next day. Or evening. I'm not even sure.

I did a quick line of coke to wake up a bit more, then reached for the trusty Yellow Pages. Odd to be on the other side of the phone, I thought with some trepidation as I listened to it ringing. But I also knew what I needed, right then, was to feel good, just to feel good.

So I did what everyone else would do in the same situation. I called an escort service. Well, maybe not *everyone* …

I wasn't even sure who or what I wanted; I just wanted to feel something, anything, to feel the way I felt when I read the novel on the bus, to feel like it was worth trying to do all these things – work, make a life, have a business, connect with people, form relationships. Have sex: that was, actually, my driving thought. The connection between sex and death has been belabored far too much in literature, but I'll add my two cents, anyway: I was coming back from the brink of death, and all I could think about was having sex.

Of having life.

They sent me a woman and a man. I guess that makes sense: when in doubt, cover all of your bases. Or maybe they were just figuring that they could get twice the fee from someone who was as confused as I must have sounded on the telephone.

They were both young, in their early twenties; I'm good at figuring that sort of thing out. They arrived separately, the woman slightly more prompt than the man. She and I had already had a Scotch from the minibar and a line from my stash by the time he arrived.

We started out right away having sex, since that was what we were all there for, all of us naked and sweating and squirming. I was feeling particularly passive, and told them as much. I have to say that they did put on a very good show. Well, that makes sense: we were in Atlantic City, after all.

So I watched the show. He sat her on his lap and fucked her. She sucked his cock. She sucked my pussy while he fucked her from behind. I participated as much as I felt like, which was really pleasant. For once, no one was demanding that I do anything, be anything, put up with anything. I could do whatever I wanted.

For two wonderful, glorious hours, that was exactly what I did. I played with myself while I watched them. He played with me while she danced around us. He kissed me while he was fucking her. She kissed me while he was fucking me. All of it nondemanding and nearly all of it in silence.

They left and I sat and smoked a cigarette alone in the darkness. After about an hour, there was a knock on the door. She had returned with some winnings from the casino downstairs.

She leaned against the doorjamb, looking embarrassed. "Hi, remember me? I'm Joy, I was here a while ago ..." Her voice trailed off.

God, she must deal with people with *real* memory deficits. Impressive ones. "I remember," I said slowly.

She gestured toward the room behind me. "I just …" She seemed to pull herself together, straightened up, and looked me in the eye. "The truth is I saw all your pills. And I wanted to be sure you're all right," she said.

I was made of stone. I had no idea how to respond. Someone I had hired had not only noticed, but cared enough to come back. She must have been thinking of it at the tables downstairs. She must have been worried. I was amazed.

I cleared my throat and moved aside. "Do you want to come in?"

She smiled, and walked in past me. "Do you have any more champagne?"

I closed the door. "Scotch okay?"

We stayed up for another couple of hours, drinking Scotch, doing lines, complaining about men, and talking about everything and nothing. I was pulling myself together then, whether I knew it or not. It was a good feeling.

By Sunday I was sore and exhausted, but somehow not as empty as I had been when I came to Atlantic City. In the end I put all of the pills back into their bottles and tucked them into my suitcase. I might have been feeling better – but not that much better. I was hedging my bets.

Maybe that's how we all live, in the end: deciding that today will not be the day that we kill ourselves.

So I got on another bus in the rain, stared out of its streaky windows all the way back to Boston, and picked up the pieces. And swore, as we all do, that I'd never fall in love again.

PRIVATE YELLOW PAGES

I was surprised, and gratified, to note that I had been missed. That my absence had upset more than just my clients. Robert had left about a hundred messages on my services; Jenny had called too, and Vivienne from the Design Group. I felt justified in my decision to wait it out.

Maybe life wasn't so bad, after all.

The clients, needless to say, showed varying levels of unhappiness at my unavailability for a couple of nights. I hadn't thought to have someone cover the phones for me, because I hadn't really been convinced that I was coming back. Some were petulant, some were angry, others were extra-demanding, as though needing to get back at me in some way.

By that time, I had organized my thinking about my profession. Clients had started falling into different categories: they were types and personalities, rather than individuals – most of them, anyway. I knew some of them as separate real people, of course; I even became friends with them.

I had quickly discovered that the men who used my service could be of service to me as well. It was like having my own private Yellow Pages – or a personal concierge service. I had, at a phone call away, doctors of all sorts, an excellent criminal lawyer (I had *his* number programmed into my telephone, just in case), club owners, someone who was "connected," various drug dealers, and a whole lot of people involved in the dot-coms, which were just coming into their own by then. I was given free tickets to concerts, entrée into political dinners, a nod at the doors of exclusive restaurants and nightclubs.

I loved it, of course. I wouldn't have been human if I hadn't. It was like a fantasy come true. Cinderella at a never-ending ball.

I knew a thing or two about fantasies, after all.

Using an escort agency is all about fantasy. I can't say that's true across the board for prostitution – it probably isn't. I suspect that when a guy picks up a woman on a street corner for a quick blow job in his front seat, he isn't imagining it to be anything other than what it is. But what I'm selling is a dream, a fantasy, the ongoing fantasy that this wonderful, beautiful, attentive woman who asks for nothing other than to spend an hour with you could conceivably be yours forever.

That is a fantasy no matter which way you look at it. First of all, no woman is sexually and emotionally attentive to the man she is with twenty-four hours a day. Real life – work, children, projects, appointments, hormones – all vie for a partner's attention, and that's not to mention the fact that most women occasionally want someone to be attentive to *them*. Not too many men like to think about that.

Never mind: the fantasy is the harem, the beautiful, always-available, always-desirable girl who makes you feel powerful, adored, manly.

The whole mindset is pretty sick, actually, but it's the mindset that we have to work with, and I do work with it. I play into that fantasy, giving my clients the girls of their dreams, assuring them how much each girl really *really* likes them. To my eternal astonishment, they always believe me.

Peter Povaklas is a case in point. He has been using my service almost since the first day I opened. And Peter waits, eternally, for the girl who will fall in love with him and make love to him forever. He goes through a lot of girls, though, because when he realizes that she's not going to be The One, he immediately starts treating her badly. Nothing hurtful or dangerous, mind you – just mean. Snapping at her, becoming more demanding, that sort of thing.

But he still calls me for girls at least twice a week, faithfully, and still somehow believes that one time, just one time, will be the right time.

Part of Peter's problem, I am told by those who visit him, is that he has no sense of a relationship (even one as well-defined and brief as a call) as being give-and-take in any way. He argues constantly with the girl (and with me, for that matter) about – well, just about anything.

"Peach said that you'd give me a long massage to start with."

"Okay, that's fine, turn on your stomach."

"Don't be stupid! You're supposed to take off your clothes first! You don't know what you're doing!"

Peter is a clock-watcher, making sure that he is not cheated out of thirty seconds of his allotted time, and indeed pushing to see if he can get far more. When a girl arrives at his place, he keeps her from calling to check in with me, making her wait, then saying that he is timing his hour from when she made the call. Stuff like that.

He really seems to have no idea that his level of churlishness might be connected to the fact that no one seems to be falling in love with him.

Timing's a tricky thing in this business. Some of my clients go by the clock, like Peter, jealously coveting each moment of what they see as "their" time. Others don't care, and in fact are happy to have a

girl leave early if she has finished what he wanted her
to do.

I had one client for a while, *very* much in demand,
who checked into a hotel in the financial district once
or twice a month and wanted a blow job with his
morning paper. Literally. He'd have a girl over there
at seven or seven-thirty in the morning. She'd knock
on the door, pick up the copy of *USA Today* that was
sitting in the hallway in front of the door, and bring
both services with her. He'd have the morning news
on the TV and be partway through his coffee and con-
tinental breakfast. There was no need to check in with
me. (I would hardly have even heard the telephone,
at that ungodly hour.) He was well-trained, paid her
upfront, no problems.

She didn't even have to undress. He'd read, she'd
kneel in front of him, loosen his robe, take out his
penis, and go to work. Five minutes later, he was tossing the newspaper down, tucking himself back in, giving her a distracted smile, his mind already moving on
to the business events of the day, and she was on her
way. Anyone who could get up that early (or stay up
that late) was more than delighted to go and see him.

Some of the girls I hire can't wait to get out of the
room. The ones who can really get away with that are
the ones who are the most strikingly beautiful, who
are drop-dead gorgeous, and have the clients amazed
that they just had sex with someone who looks like a

supermodel. Let's face it, it's not all that surprising. The reality of our world is that gorgeous women can get away with almost anything they want.

Some of them rush the client: what do you want, where do you want it, here's the condom, let's get on with it. Some of the clients appreciate that, actually – there's no need to manufacture meaningless small-talk, no awkwardness, no need to pretend. It's all about sex.

But the ones who want the fantasy, they're the ones who want the girl there for the duration. And it seems to me, more and more, that that's what guys are looking for.

Someone used to say to me – it might have been Jen, or maybe Lily, they were the two most introspective employees I've had – that the way she saw it, she was being paid for an hour of her time. The client could spend the time doing whatever he wanted – talking, playing stupid mind games, fucking. She never left before the hour was up unless the client wanted her to. Both Jen and Lily accumulated a fair number of regulars, so whoever it was must have been doing something right.

The ones like Peter, the ones who like to argue, for them that's part of the experience. The power, the control, the kind of feeling they get by winning an argument. I think it's a weird way of getting off, but if it's what works, it's what works.

God knows they'll argue with me, endlessly.

It starts with the negotiation over who they will see that night. Guys sometimes call in advance and request someone particular ahead of time, making a date, as it were. But, more often than not, they call and order a girl like they're ordering from the Chinese restaurant down the block. So a typical conversation might sound a little like this:

"Hi, Peach, it's Hubert."

"Hey, Hubert, how are you? What can I do for you?"

"Is Lisa around tonight?" So much for the pleasantries. I'm fine, thanks for asking.

A quick glance at my cheat sheet. I know that Lisa isn't working, but that's not going to keep me from doing business with Hubert. What I'm wondering is who I have that's enough like Lisa to be able to send instead of her. "You know, Hubert, she's not around tonight, but Gloria's getting out of class at eight and I can have her go straight over to your place after that."

He sounds petulant. "Who's Gloria?"

"You've seen her before," I tell him, my voice firm and reassuring. "She's a junior at Northeastern University. She comes from Kansas, has that accent, you know, a pretty Midwestern girl. You saw her a few weeks ago. Long brown hair?" I end on a hopeful note.

Hubert's not having any of it. "I don't remember," he snaps, and there's irritation in his voice. "Can't you call Lisa?"

I sigh. It's the girl's night off, and they somehow think that if I called her she'd be delighted to cancel whatever plans she has and rush over to fuck them. Like their office could call them on a Saturday night to go in and work on some report. "She's away on a ski trip with her parents," I say, glibly, the lie coming quickly and easily. They always do. It's one of my strengths, my ability to find immediate plausible lies.

The "parents" part is key: there's an element of wholesomeness that clients expect, something they never find to be in contradiction with what the girl happens to do for a living. There are some guys who actually believe that this is the first and only time she's tried it.

Like I said, it's a fantasy world out there.

"I think you'd have a really good time with Gloria. She really liked you, Hubert. She told me I could send her to you anytime. She doesn't say that about everyone."

There is a slight pause while he regroups. "I don't know, Peach. Tell me again what she looks like?"

There's another call coming in, and this one threatens to be a long one. "Hold on just one second, Hubert," I say, and switch lines before he has a chance to respond. "Hello?"

"Hi, um, I wanted to know if you could, um, like, come over tonight."

I take a deep breath. Even though the ad says I'm an agency, there are always guys that imagine it's a blonde with D cups answering the phone, working solo. I guess that for some of the ads, that's true. "Sir, did you want to spend some time with a young lady this evening?"

"Um, yes."

"And where are you located, sir?" No one says sir anymore. Except for people who come from the South. Or from repressive families of origin. I guess I hit it on both tries.

"Um, I'm at the Sheraton, in Newton. I – I don't live in Boston."

Hubert would just have to wait, I decide. "Can I have your name to verify it with the front desk, sir?"

Long pause. Either he's a problem or he is just embarrassed. I sense the latter, so I reassure him. "It's entirely confidential, sir. It's just to ensure the safety of the young lady who comes to see you."

That gets him. He's clearly surprised that he might be seen as something of a threat. "Oh. Yes. Okay. Right. No, that's, like, fine."

"Very good, sir. Just give me the information – your name and your room number – and I'll call you right back."

He does, and I click back to Hubert. "Sorry to keep you on hold. That was my mother. I couldn't just hang up on her. What were you asking?"

Hubert has had time to think, not a good thing. "You're sure that Lisa isn't back yet? When will she be back?"

I don't want to lose the call, and I can feel him hesitating, feel it slipping away. "Hubert, I honestly don't know. They're in Europe, in the Alps. Skiing. It might not be for a while, and she'll be overloaded with course work when she gets back. But I know you'd like to see someone tonight, and I'd love to have you see Gloria. She's got long brown hair, I know you'll remember her. Green eyes." (Thank goodness for contact lenses.) "She's 36-24-32, she's twenty-two, she's beautiful and really, really sweet. I know that you liked her, and she really liked you a lot."

Come *on*, Hubert. Get with the program here. I know you're going to ask for her. You know you're going to ask for her. Let's stop dancing around each other and just get on with it.

"Oh, okay, Peach." He still doesn't sound convinced.

That's as close as I'm going to get with him. "I'll have her give you a call, Hubert. I know you'll have a good time. It will …"

He interrupts. "When, exactly?"

I told him she gets out of class at eight, I remind myself. I've always been pretty good at remembering my inventions. "Probably about eight-thirty."

"That's an hour from now!" If a person can be said to howl, Hubert just howled. I sigh. He'll survive. "Yes, she doesn't get out of class until then. I'll have her call you, Hubert. I promise."

I disconnect before he can say anything else, check that the new guy is legit, then call him back. "So, Jack – can I call you Jack? – this is Peach calling back from Avanti. Thanks for your patience. Now, tell me a little about yourself. Is there any particular type of young lady you have in mind to see this evening?"

Some nights, I simply do *not* get paid enough for what I have to do.

THE CLIENT FROM HELL

Even though clients blend into types, rather than individuals, Peter Povaklas stands out. Because he's demanding. Because he's pathetic. And, maybe, because he's hopeful. Peter doesn't give up on his dream, no matter how far he is from realizing it.

He does all the wrong things, naturally. He invites girls to go down to New York City with him and participate in orgies, and then when they do, he complains that they're not monogamous, or asks them to pick up the tab at the pre-orgy dinner. I'm not sure exactly what the etiquette is in that sort of situation, but I'm pretty sure that he's not following it. I'll have to look in my big white Emily Post book sometime.

He's nasty, coarse, and boorish, and then complains that girls don't want to spend extra time – unpaid time, mind you – in his wonderful presence. He insults them and is subsequently surprised when they don't gush over him. He's astonished when I tell him that someone has chosen not to see him at all, something I've had to do on more than one occasion.

But at the bottom of all the nonsense I believe there's this sad little boy who just wants the house and the white picket fence and the perfect wife waiting for him at the end of the day. It's not his fault that he's fifty years out of date. It's not his fault that he can't see that what he's doing isn't going to get him there, never in a million years. He's the product of his background as much as I'm the product of mine, and his background doesn't allow him to be sensitive, caring, or respectful.

I once heard insanity defined as doing the same thing over and over and expecting a different result. That's Peter Povaklas. He's caught in this little centrifuge that just spins him around and around, doing the same thing over and over and being constantly surprised that the same routine hasn't worked yet another time.

He's a long-term relationship for me. He'll be here when I finally close my doors. Me and Peter Povaklas.

Some of the girls don't mind him. Aside from being demanding and fussy, he's really not all that difficult. He doesn't have people swinging from chandeliers – for him it's pretty much vanilla sex. And the girls learned how to handle him, how to insist that they call me right away so he can't play his games around the phone. One night Cilla stopped by to have a drink and drop off her fee, and she told me about a conversation she'd had with Peter. It went something like this.

PETER: Okay, come in, let me see what you're wearing.

CILLA: Hi, Peter, I just need to check in with Peach first.

PETER: Just give me a minute first, okay? You're like an adding machine. I want to be sure that I want to see you first. Let me see what you look like.

CILLA: You know what I look like, Peter. I'll spin around as much as you want, but I have to call Peach first.

PETER: But –

CILLA (*cutting him off*): But you know Peach won't send me here anymore if I don't call. She says that I waste a lot of time and she'll send someone who's going to watch the clock more. So let me call her so I can keep seeing you, okay, Peter?

PETER (*grumbling*): You all watch the clock.

CILLA (*sweetly, reaching for the phone*): You can always ask for another hour, Peter. That would be more relaxing …

PETER: What do you mean, an extra hour?
You think I'm made of money, or
something? Go ahead, fine, if that's
all you can think about, make your
fucking call.

Nice way to start an intimate sexual encounter with
somebody – but what do I know? Whatever works.
If I've learned anything from this business, it's that –
whatever works.

Some of the girls aren't as good with Peter, or with
anyone for that matter, when they start demanding
more. Most of us, after all, were raised to be nice, and
it's hard to drop that polite façade we cultivate, even
in the face of rudeness, even when someone is taking advantage of them. It's difficult to stay firm and
sweet at the same time. There are so many of them
out there, guys who are predators in the smallest ways,
who live to take advantage of someone like a college
girl trying to make a living.

So I'm clear about boundaries. Very clear. When a
girl starts liking a client too much, I try to ease her off
him. I'm not an idiot; I'm not going to shoot myself in
the foot and not send her if no one else can go, or if
he asks for her; but, by and large, when I can, I try to
back them off. Because it's when you start liking a client that the boundaries get blurred. And that's never
a good thing.

My own boundaries started to get blurred a little when Benjamin came back into my life.

Benjamin. I'd met him during the first year I was in business for myself. He was driving taxis and playing in a garage band called Mnemonic. I'd been out somewhere – funny how I can't remember exactly where – and was coming back late at night. Benjamin was driving the taxi. I was a little drunk, a little high, and I invited him upstairs with me.

There aren't that many taxi drivers I've met who resist that sort of invitation.

Benjamin stayed around, though. The next morning, he fixed my VCR so that the 12:00 digits would stop blinking, and cooked me breakfast, which was really a feat when you consider that I didn't have exactly what one would consider a well-stocked pantry. My idea of dinner preparation was having takeaway numbers on speed dial. He left to return his cab and go to a rehearsal, but he smiled when he did.

Like he already knew he'd be back.

With Benjamin, I drifted into something not entirely unlike a relationship – to paraphrase *The Hitchhiker's Guide to the Galaxy* – without really thinking much about what was happening. He was just there. He'd come and go as he pleased, sometimes staying with me for a couple of days, then not coming around for a week. I let him have a key more out of apathy than anything else.

Odd, when you consider it: what eventually became the most important relationship of my life didn't exactly start out auspiciously. Actually, it barely started at all. One day I considered myself single, and then, almost imperceptibly, Benjamin was there.

Sometimes.

The sometimes part of it became wearing. Not that I was seeing anyone else, particularly, but I just felt like I was always reacting, an observer in my own life rather than a participant. And I don't do well with that. Jesse should have taught me about that, if no one else had.

But it seemed that the more the business blossomed, the more I was willing to take a passive role in my personal life.

When he was there, Benjamin was fun. If there were people over, he'd hang out with us, play board games, have a drink, get high. I remember deep discussions from that time that probably weren't all that deep at all, but sure as hell felt that way at the time. That's a high all in itself. There's nothing like solving the world's problems in a single night to make you feel good.

To be honest, it wasn't the best time in my life, and I was grasping at straws for a little happiness. I had these ideas that once the business was up and running and I was Someone, someone cool and hip and popular, that everything would be good, and I'd be happy. All the shadows would be gone and I'd feel content, competent, and beautiful.

Sometimes I felt that maybe I did have a handle on it, that I was just a breath away, a footstep away, a thought away from happiness.

Then it would be gone, as if I had never even been close at all.

Part of that construct, for me, involved being in some sort of relationship, not that casual sex is something to be sneezed at, mind you: I've always seen it as an integral and fulfilling part of life, and after Jesse left it became a mainstay of my existence.

Being popular, I hadn't had any problems securing a partner for a night, a week, a couple of months even – nice guys, some of them, though their names and faces seem a little blurry to me now.

But I was also beginning to realize that at some point the soirée is over and the people go home. And you're stuck with you.

Waking up to the prospect of dealing with a dozen emotionally needy men wasn't exactly what I had in mind when I closed my eyes and imagined something I could call happiness.

Benjamin wasn't what I had imagined, either, but I was beginning to understand – and, more importantly, accept – that nothing ever is. I think I was important to him, but I was on a list of other important things, like the band and the Red Sox and work. He fit me in, and that was exactly what it felt like: being fit in.

I didn't like being part of a list.

We drifted like that for some time, me too lethargic and unable to commit to make him leave, him too busy and unable to commit to want to stay for very long.

I'd see other people I knew, my friends, doing the same thing – drifting. What had happened to dating? What had happened to being a couple, and being okay with being a couple?

Even Jen, who by then was fast becoming one of my closest friends, even she was equivocating about the whole thing. She was seeing Luis, then she wasn't seeing Luis, then she was seeing Luis again. It was as if we had all lost some sort of internal compass that our parents' generation had been able to grasp and use for guidance. We'd lost it, and all sense of where we were going.

So Benjamin came and went, and I spent days and nights talking to Siddhartha and Court, wondering how it was that I had come to such a pass, where my most significant relationships were with my cats.

In the meantime business was booming. We were in the mid-nineties, and little boys were making fortunes out of Web sites they thought up one night when they'd done too much coke (I know – I was there for a couple of them) and spending some of their fortunes on girls who never would have looked at them before they had dollar signs after their names. We were all doing well then.

Sometimes I'd drink too much Pinot Grigio and complain, but Jenny always laughed at me. She had a cat, too, with some computer-related name I can't remember, though what I do remember is her laughing eyes over the rim of her wineglass. "Never underestimate the value of a relationship with a cat," she said, nodding wisely. "With a cat, you know where you stand."

I just know that after a few days with them, I was always looking forward to Benjamin showing up, and that's *never* a good position to be in. When you start wanting him to be there more than he wants to be there, it's a problem.

Robert offered to take me away for a long weekend. Lily offered to distract me; she even slept in my living room for a week so that if Benjamin came over I wouldn't be tempted. Cilla offered to see him for free so that I could really despise him. So my friends were solidly on my side.

Unfortunately, my heart wasn't, and that's the most treacherous friend of all.

LET'S SEE ...
HOW CAN I PROVE I DID IT?

I needed to get out of town.

Benjamin hadn't shown up in over a week. The clients were particularly annoying, the sun was bright, and everything in my universe was screaming, "Road trip!"

Jenny was up for it. She almost always was, and she usually had ideas about what to do. "Ogunquit," she decided.

It sounded like a good plan. Ogunquit is a small town on Maine's southern coast, very much a summer people sort of place; winters are cold, with slate gray skies and waves to match, but in the summer all the antique shops, bed and breakfasts, and theaters open up, and the place comes alive with riotous colors and a multitude of languages. It's also something of a gay mecca, which I find attractive. Any place with a live-and-let-live motto is fine in my book.

Best of all, Ogunquit is only a few hours' drive north of Boston. It's like a vacation without commitment.

Ogunquit means "beautiful place by the sea" in the Micmac language, and as we pulled in that Friday afternoon, it was clear that it was aptly named. The shore snakes around so that you get tantalizing glimpses of it from the road, promising relief from stress and the workaday world. We drove through town first, Jen swearing at the pedestrians walking in front of us. I just looked out the window, passing the creepy Leavitt Theatre with its peeling white paint and green window boxes, Maxwell's Pub with its dubious promise of karaoke, the Mad Hatter Bakery.

She was impatient to get out of the car. "Is this place okay?"

"Sure, anything's fine." We got out at the Hotel Viking, with its wide balconies on two floors overlooking the ocean and water on both sides. It sat on a cul-de-sac that ended at the beach. We threw our bags in the room without really noticing it; Jen was eager for the ocean.

She told me once that her dream was to sail around the world. "You know, take two years off, just go. Let the water be the only rhythm in your life. You couldn't come back the same person you were when you left."

And my own dreams? At the time, they were ill-defined, carrying words like happiness and contentment. Of course, I hadn't met Sam, then. He's brought me all the happiness and contentment there is in the world.

We walked on the beach for a while and then wandered back into town, stopping off at the food market for bottles of wine that we left in our room when we changed for dinner. Ogunquit's that kind of place. It's not like Boston, where you have to change for dinner. In Ogunquit, you want to. We ate duck and asparagus and risotto at a tiny restaurant-cum-bed-and-breakfast and shared a bottle of wine with dinner. Jen insisted on cognac after, and we were slightly tipsy by the time we made it back through the thinning summer crowds to the hotel.

The wide porch outside our room beckoned. It was dark, and the surf was making small hissing sounds on the sand. The perfect night for a glass of wine, or five.

Neither of us had a bottle opener.

I was on the phone in a flash. Never mind that it wasn't the Ritz; I could make the desk clerk into a concierge, I decided, by sheer willpower.

The clerk downstairs could not only locate a bottle opener; he would be happy to deliver it personally, seeing that he was getting off his shift in a few minutes.

I stretched lazily across the bed. "Why not? Bring three wineglasses, too, won't you?" Jen was sitting on the deck, her eyes closed, listening to the ocean. Or maybe sleeping.

The knock at the door came about ten minutes later. He might have been all of twenty. He moved with the awkwardness of adolescence and, I swear, he already had an erection.

We were already well on our way to being toasted, and the wine kept the glow on. Yards away from us, the surf hissed and murmured. Boston could have been a million miles away, and I was feeling playful, very playful.

Front Desk Boy (I can't for the life of me remember his name; indeed, I consider it a triumph that I remember anything about that evening at all) was obviously happy to be sitting and drinking with us. He appeared to have no ambitions beyond working at the Viking Hotel, and that was fine with me, too: I was tired of pseudointellectuals.

Jen must have been feeling playful, too. She was stretched out on a chaise lounge, sipping her wine, her eyes still shut. "So, do you know what she does for a living?" she asked Front Desk Boy, gesturing toward me. I giggled.

He looked eager. "No, what?"

Jen smiled without opening her eyes. "She's a madam."

I looked at Front Desk Boy. He was still smiling eagerly, but he was starting to look nervous, as if he had already been the butt of many such jokes and was anticipating being laughed at again. He twisted the wineglass in his hands. "Yeah, right," he offered half-heartedly.

"Ask her," said Jen.

He peered at me. I was dressed in a slinky blue dress I'd picked up for a small fortune at a boutique in Harvard Square, and had slipped out of my high heels. He was impressed, but not enough to let go of his insecurity. "Is it true?"

I patted the chaise next to me. "Come over here," I suggested.

He came, smelling of soap and sweat and some repellent aftershave that he'd probably doused himself in before coming upstairs with the glasses and the corkscrew. He was still in the terrible throes of acne. I decided not to think about his age. He was old enough to work, wasn't he? I slid a hand onto his knee. "I'm a madam," I confirmed, softly, looking into his eyes, "down in Boston."

"Really?" His defenses were crumbling. He wanted so badly to believe me.

I moved my hand over his thigh, gently, but not too gently. "Really," I said, and leaned into him. It didn't take too much. After all the drinking we'd been doing, I was pretty much in a leaning frame of mind.

Front Desk Boy gave up. There's just so long a man can hold on to his pride. His arm went up around my shoulders and he bent down to kiss me. It wasn't exactly what I had planned to do, but why not? I kissed him back with some enthusiasm. I think the last time I kissed someone that young, I was sixteen myself.

It was a lot of fun.

Once he had decided to go for it, Front Desk Boy showed himself to have a great deal of enthusiasm, as well as some surprising creativity. We both abandoned the wineglasses fairly quickly, passing the bottle back and forth instead.

We came up for air once we'd finished the bottle. Jenny was watching us, a clear expression of amusement on her face. She had opened another bottle and handed it to me. "Enjoy," she said.

Front Desk Boy had decided that it was time for conversation. "So," he said to Jen, "what do you do in Boston?"

She smiled even more broadly. "I work for her," she said, gesturing toward me.

He blinked. "You mean –"

She nodded. "I'm a callgirl."

His eyes widened. "Oh my God." He looked from her to me as the information sank in. I could imagine him at school or the pizza place the next day. On second thought, they probably wouldn't believe him. Poor Front Desk Boy. "Oh my God," he said again.

Jen seemed to think the whole thing was a joke. She sat back, a smile on her face, closing her eyes again.

I, however, was still in the mood to play. I moved slightly so he could lean past me until he was lying on the chaise lounge, and then I straddled him. His T-shirt came off quite easily, and I was running my fingertips up and down his chest, a singularly naked chest. I could feel his erection through his pants, through my dress, and I was suddenly in love with this boy, in love with this moment, where things could happen just because they felt good, where nothing was orchestrated and planned and paid for.

I pulled my dress off over my head, still straddling him, and he gasped with pleasure. I leaned down and ran my tongue from his collarbone to his chin and I could feel him quivering beneath me. He reached around and unfastened my demi cup bra with a lot more dexterity than I would have given him credit for. So he had been down this path once or twice before, after all.

I found the thought oddly arousing.

I reached down between us and pulled at his pants. The button and the zipper opened quickly and easily, and he lifted his hips so that he could wriggle out of them.

I felt a tap on my shoulder. Jen, her evening bag in one hand, was standing next to me, rummaging in it and finally pulling something out of it. A condom. I nodded my thanks, then laughed out loud for no reason at all, simply feeling happy, unburdened, and alive. She was still smiling as she went back to her place, took a drink of wine, and closed her eyes again. I couldn't tell if her disinterest was real or contrived.

On the other hand, I really didn't care all that much, one way or the other.

I was back on top of him, and now Front Desk Boy was more than ready to get on with things. He held my hips as he lifted his and slid his cock into me. By now I was very wet and it felt good going in. I moaned and started moving up and down on him. He let go of my hips, reached up and grabbed my breasts, pumping into me, his cock hard and young and wonderfully filling.

And he went on forever. I came at last, gasping, collapsing on top of him and trembling all over. Then he had lifted me off the chaise, laying me down directly on the deck and was on top of me, ramming his cock back into my pussy, wet now with my own cum, pounding me into the floor and sweating and grunting on top of me. I moved with him, and impossibly had two more orgasms, one right after the other, before he lifted me up off the deck with the power of his final thrust as he came.

We lay there for a few minutes together, both of us just trying to catch our breath, until he finally sat up. There was sweat running down his back; I was bathing in it. He neatly removed the condom and flicked it into the wastebasket just outside the door, where we'd been discarding corks and empty bottles. Then he stood up in one lithe movement, stretched, and reached for his clothes, a man who can fuck and who knows enough not to discuss it afterward. Better still, who can assess the situation, see that in a nonsexual context he is clearly surplus to requirement and make a graceful exit. Front Desk Boy was worth his weight in gold. I nodded at him appreciatively.

He grinned back. "So," he said, and I waited for pearls of wisdom. Someone who has this much sense is surely going to make some elegant, or at least meaningful, postcoital observation. "So," he said again, "how can I prove to people that I just fucked a madam?"

* * * * * *

"You brought that one on yourself." Jen said as we got ready for bed. There was one king-sized bed in the room; I couldn't remember the last time I'd slept in one.

"He was so *young*," I said, either by way of excuse of explanation, I wasn't sure.

"He had pimples," she observed, acidly. She had brushed her teeth and was sliding into a black T-shirt and boxer shorts. "What is it with French people and black clothes, anyway?" I demanded, à propos of nothing.

"People in New York wear black all the time, too," she said. "And London. Maybe it's a city thing."

"I live in a city," I said, looking at the white cotton nightgown that she had helped me into. Okay, so I was clearly a lot drunker than I had thought I was.

"Not according to your wardrobe, you don't," she said, the smile back in her voice.

She shut off the light, and we lay in the darkness together for a moment before she started giggling. "What?" I asked.

She turned over to face me. "So," she said, fighting to keep her voice serious, imitating Front Desk Boy, "How do I prove that I fucked a madam?"

I started laughing then, too, far more than the joke warranted — but then again, that's one of the beauties of being drunk. Everything is far funnier.

"Like this," I said without thinking, putting my arms around her and pulling her closer to me, and then we were kissing, soft lips on soft lips, mine still bruised and tender from the Front Desk Boy, hers fresh from her toothpaste.

The kiss lasted about three centuries and three seconds all at once. Jen pulled away, slightly, and started to say something, but I put my finger to her lips. "Shh," I said. "Don't say anything."

She didn't. In fact, she opened her lips to my finger and pulled it inside, sucking gently and then harder. I moved my hips closer to hers, wriggling against her. I pulled my finger out of her mouth and moved it down her body, rubbing her breast and pinching her nipple through the cotton fabric of the T-shirt. She started to say something again, but I leaned over her and put my mouth on hers, a little more insistent this time, my tongue probing.

Her arms came up, locked around me and she pulled me on top of her, her kisses now as insistent as mine. Our breasts moved against each other, and her breathing was ragged as she fumbled with the ribbons on my nightgown. It didn't work, and we both started giggling again. She brought both hands up and simply ripped the front of it. "I love it when you're assertive," I gasped.

Our hands were all over each other, smoothing, caressing, pinching. Jen slid down in the bed, her lips and tongue on my breasts, teasing my nipples, sucking on them. I squirmed under her, but she held me down as she teased and tickled me. I undulated under her, half-breathless, twisting and turning and then I was the one on top, slithering down over her until my lips were on her pussy and she was the one moaning and struggling, her fingers entwined in my hair.

I came up for air and we ground our hips against each other. She reached between my legs and slipped a finger inside my pussy, then another, moving them in and out, rubbing my clit, then plunging back in. By then I was panting so loud that I might as well have been shouting. She sighed with delight and dived down so that she could taste my pussy again, and I wrapped my legs around her head and squeezed.

It was well after three in the morning when we stopped, exhausted, still tipsy. She stood in the door to the bathroom, tipping the last of the wine from the bottle down her throat. I was examining my shredded nightgown.

Jen laughed and started singing. "Welcome to the asylum …"

I sat up, reaching for my cigarettes. "I was born in South Carolina," I said, flicking out the match and tossing it into the ashtray. I inhaled, then slowly blew the smoke out into the room. "Someone famous – I can't remember who it was – said that South Carolina is too small for a good-sized plantation and too big for an insane asylum."

She came back to the bed, took the cigarette from me, and put it out in the ashtray. Leaning across me to put out the light, she said, "Are you sure about that?"

Then we didn't say anything at all for a very long time.

148

CATERING BY ANY OTHER NAME

Christmas was fast approaching, and my mother was wondering, at great length and in a whole series of letters, if she was ever going to see me again.

Her anxiety didn't have anything to do with the religious significance of the event. My family have always been lukewarm Lutherans, and religion has never played a tremendous role in my life.

Sometimes I've wished that it had.

Not enough to convert, mind you. Not enough to do anything about it. Just enough to wonder, and, at some level, to envy.

So I knew that my mother wasn't asking me to come see her because we had fond memories of midnight mass at Christmas or anything like that. No – my mother wanted to know what was going on.

Ah, yes. The $64,000 question. What is it that you do for a living, Abby?

With anyone who calls me Abby, I know I have to be careful. We're in the real world here, and it is, of course, a tricky question.

For a long time, I told people that I had my own catering business. This covers a lot: I'm on the phone for much of the evening, coordinating whatever it is that I'm catering at any given time; I'm on the phone during the day, sometimes setting up events, contacting the women who work for me as cooks and waitresses. I don't have a specific place of business; it's a distribution company, as they liked to say in the 1990s. It made a lot of sense to most people, who would nod and then move on.

And that was, and still is, the best thing about it: the fact that it doesn't invite a whole lot of questions, for the excellent reason that it's simply not that interesting.

Imagine the cocktail party, the snippets of bright conversation, the superficial smiles. "And what do *you* do?"

"I own a small catering service."

The smile stays frozen in place. "Oh! How – nice!" If the person is trapped with me, they'll then wrack their brains for some question that they can ask. There aren't a lot. "So, do you like doing that?"

I shrug indifferently. "It's okay. It's not all that interesting."

They drift away. Guaranteed.

So it's a safe haven of sorts, this catering business. I even had some stationery made up at one time, just letterhead, something I could use for official correspondence when necessary. I told my mother I had a catering business, and once she got past the fact that I couldn't cook ("Mom, I have people who do that for me"), she was fine with it.

Most of the time.

When meeting a friend's parent, during the brief time I was on the board at the library, I got glib and practiced. I was a caterer. Hell, I was a great caterer.

Jeremy Burns was some sort of marketing guru. There were a lot of them around back then in the 1990s, guys whose business was to tell the dot-com wizards how to spend more money getting more famous for doing whatever it was they did. I'd run into him when I was looking for used books at the Avenue Victor Hugo shop on Newbury Street, and we'd shared a coffee or two, nothing romantic, just someone I knew casually. When Jeremy asked me what I did, the answer slipped smoothly off my tongue. "I run a small catering business." He asked me for my card, and I feigned a surprised professional air, assuring him that I had just run out and was getting more printed. I gave him my work number because my private line was having some problems, and ran into him a few more times, as one invariably does in

151

a city the size of Boston, and didn't give it another thought.

The call came on a Tuesday. "Hello?"

"Hi, um, is this Avanti?"

My agency has a name, but I rarely use it except for promotional purposes. "Yes, it is," I said. "How can I help you, sir?"

"Is this Abby? It sounds like you. This is Jeremy Burns. We – um – we met over on Newbury Street a few weeks ago, I was the guy talking about Faulkner ..."

The true way to my heart? Talk about Faulkner. But something wasn't right here. How had Jeremy found out about my business? Did he want to have a call put out to him? I was already in madam mode, answering the telephone and anticipating the needs; this came a little out of left field. "I remember you," I said, finally, a little helplessly. I had no idea what else to say.

"Well, good. You sound busy, I won't take up a lot of your time. But I have this little soirée I'm organizing –"

Oh, goodie, I thought. An invitation. All is clear. I even preened myself a bit. Maybe there was an attraction there, after all.

"– and I wondered if you could put together something light for, say, thirty people? Not a meal or anything like that, and I'm not into the whole Asian fusion thing, but just hors d'oeuvres, maybe

152

something creative. I'll have a full bar there too, with a couple of bartenders and I think they send someone extra, so maybe just three or four people serving? What do you think? I mean, you're the expert here. It's for two weeks from Saturday. Whatever you think is good, that'll work for me."

Oops. Big oops. "Jeremy, I'm putting you on hold for a minute, I'll be right back." Let him think I'm checking my calendar. I took a deep breath, and then suddenly saw the humor of it all and laughed out loud. I felt like I had been caught with my hand in the cookie jar. That'll teach you, I thought, and reconnected with him. "Hey, you know what, we're booked through the end of next month. I'm glad you called, though."

If he was heartbroken, he managed to restrain himself from showing it. "That's too bad. Well, I've got some other guys I use. I just thought …"

"No problem," I said briskly. There was another call coming in, and business was, after all, business. "Good luck with the party."

He had another thought. "Hey, Abby, maybe you'd like to come anyway?"

Ah, no, thanks. Maybe pick up some more catering customers? I don't think so. "I'll be pretty busy with things here," I said, truthfully. "Gotta go, Jeremy. I have another call coming in. It was nice talking to you."

I hadn't used the catering line on my mother in several years. I also hadn't visited her in that time. I thought about her, her house, and her conversation. I thought about the de rigeur society parties that would be part of the Christmas-in-Charleston postcard experience my mother would impose on me, the sherries drunk with elderly rich people in front of too-hot fireplaces, the goodwill and cheer that I'd have to sustain without anything but alcohol to sustain me. I thought about it, had another glass of wine and thought about it some more – and came to the conclusion that there was no way I was going home for Christmas.

* * * * * *

It was snowing when the taxi dropped me off at the airport. At least, I thought grimly, there shouldn't be any snow at home, so I had one thing going for me.

Home was, and has always been, Charleston, South Carolina. No matter how long I stayed in the North, that was where my roots were, where my persona came from.

My mother certainly was passionate about her roots. I have to give her that. There are only a handful of names in Charleston that matter – and she has one of them, her marriage to my father notwithstanding. Upon his death, she regained her own name, which I suspect she regretted ever having put aside.

She still lived in the Italianate house on South Battery Street where I was raised. It was both a dream and a nightmare to grow up in. The requisite southern verandahs, balustrades, and ornamentation looked better on a wedding cake than on a house.

I make fun of Charleston, but it made me who I am, and who I was until I left for Emerson College, Boston, and the pleasurable anonymity of a university town.

I am the child of my past and I'm as stubborn as the best of them. Maybe that was why I was here: I wasn't willing to let my mother, or my past, keep me from claiming my present. I had a life, a life that I loved; and my hometown was part of who I was. It was time for my past and my present to connect, for the circle to close. So it was my own stubbornness that had brought me here, the stubbornness of my people, the stubbornness of the marshes and the wind and the voices of Charleston's past.

Fretting about me is and always has been one of her favorite pastimes. She fretted about my grades, my boyfriends, the hems on my skirts. Once I moved to Boston, she fretted that I wasn't eating enough, that my laundry wasn't done properly, that I was giving Siddhartha and Court the wrong brand of cat food.

Let alone what I was doing for a living.

She met me at the airport, brisk and moving quickly as usual. I've never been able to understand, much less imitate, my mother's level of energy and action. "The car is parked over here. What do you have to carry? It's good to see you, dear, and isn't it cold?"

We sat in front of the tremendous fireplace in the living room of the Italianate house on South Battery. I was drinking a glass of Chardonnay; my mother was doing what she called "catching up," which meant sharing a year's worth of local gossip with me.

My mother has her own pipeline, it seems, to the upper-crust Brahmins of Boston society, and is more than a little disappointed that I have not taken my place among them. I bring up my catering business. She counters with the idea of going back to school. I reiterate my commitment to my business. "Maybe you think that catering is beneath me," I say, provocatively.

She wrinkles her diminutive nose. "No one is accusing you of *catering*, dear," she says, her hands delicate as she balances her teacup. The china is so fine it glows translucently in the firelight. "That would indeed be beneath you."

And so I learned that she knew, but I learned nothing else, for my mother is not one to confront, to look too hard or too closely at any of the parts of life she finds messy or inconvenient. Every little problem can be smoothed over with a smile; every major problem can be ignored. It was an approach that had served her well through all of her life, and she wasn't about to give up on it now.

All the same, I was grumpy. Maybe I had really wanted a confrontation. My friend Tammy, who is a lesbian, told me once of her disappointment when she went home to break the news to her family. "I thought I'd shock them," she said. "I thought they'd all be horrified, disown me, be embarrassed, *something*. But they took it so well. It was an amazing anticlimax to the whole ordeal." Perhaps I was feeling the same way, daring my mother to force me to tell her what I was doing, trying to force her hand. I'm not even sure why. Maybe getting angry would have made me feel like I was, at long last, her equal.

Is any daughter ever her mother's equal in her own mind?

Charleston did its usual Christmas thing, white holly berries on the doors, choirs singing in the streets, parties with hot mulled wine, all very Dickensian, and I found myself fading further and further away from it all. My mother and I decorated a tremendous Christmas tree that soared up two stories in our tiled foyer; friends of hers came to sip punch and hot buttered rum and talk about each other. On Christmas morning, we opened carefully selected presents. Mine was a silver locket that I wear to this day.

It wasn't that it wasn't beautiful; it was. It wasn't that we weren't getting along after our own superficial

Jenny Angell

fashion. We were. But I was finally acknowledging that I simply didn't belong there, and perhaps I hadn't, in fact, for a very long time.

I got back to Boston and sat in snarling traffic all the way through the Callahan-Sumner Tunnel from the airport into the city. The taxi driver was less than loquacious, and that was fine with me.

I was home.

* * * * * *

In the end, you choose your family. Not the one you're born with, that you're tied to with a stranglehold of shared pasts and uncertain futures, but the people you choose to make your family.

I sat in my living room and looked at Robert and Luis and Jenny and Lily and Benjamin, with Siddhartha and Court purring nearby, and I felt like purring, too. The ties that bound us all together were fragile – more fragile than any of us thought – but they were real, they were chosen, and they were conscious. And maybe, in the end, that's all that anyone needs.

158

BUSINESS AND FAMILY

Talking of how you describe your profession to people brings me nicely and emphatically back to the present.

Sam loves the park. What is it, is there something encoded into the DNA of every child at birth, that they're drawn to these places of sand, swings, jungle gyms, and inane chatter? I can think of a lot of places, kid-friendly places, I'd rather go – a walk on the beach, an adventure on a farm, a trip on the river – but no, it's the park, it's always the park.

There's something to be said, I suppose, for consistency.

When school is out, or on weekends, we go nearly every day that the weather is good. I bring a magazine and my cell phone, along with all the paraphernalia that goes with having children: feeder cups, a snack to hold him over, and of course Band-Aids.

159

Usually the magazine is ignored, since Sam appears to require my close attention to all of his feats, including the most mundane. "Look, Mom, watch me go down the slide!"

"I'm watching!"

"Mommy! Not fair! You didn't *see* me!"

"I saw you, Sam, I saw you!"

"Mom! Watch me swing! Look how high I can go!"

"Very nice, dear."

Such are our usual conversations. So I bring things with me, hoping that this will be the day when my child will magically develop some self-sufficiency and I can actually read. Never happens.

The cell phone, however, is a different story.

I talk with the other mommies, of course. And (to my initial and complete surprise) that's an accepted category in which to find oneself – "Mommy." We don't talk about what we do outside of being a mother. We don't even talk about our homes, our significant others, or anything that is unrelated to diapers and rashes and fevers.

We talk about our children.

Here, I don't need to trot out my tired catering story. Being Sam's mommy is quite enough for them.

We sit on a bench, the sun slanting down pleasantly through the trees, the kids all nicely occupied. Maybe one of them trips and needs a hug; maybe someone has harsh words with someone else; but that's the extent of the potential disasters, the potential acrimony. Birds chirp overhead. I eat a few soggy animal crackers and pay attention to the conversation, which has to do with Marianne's daughter's teething problems.

And then my phone rings.

"Hello?"

"Hey, Peach. It's Pete Povaklas."

Oh, great. My best client from hell, and how does one disguise this particular conversation? "Hi, Pete," I say, cautiously. The other mommies are still talking in the background, their voices politely muted so that I can carry on my conversation.

"Peach, I want someone new. I mean, really new. Someone who will appreciate me."

If I were at home in my study right now I know what I'd say. I'd tell him that he would be appreciated a lot more if he treated the girls with a little more respect. It's a conversation that we have on a semiregular basis. But in view of the circumstances ... "Sure thing," I say, noncommittally. "I'm not at my desk right now. Can you call me back later and we'll take care of it then?"

Wishful thinking. "No, Peach," he says irritably. "I'm tired of always talking about something later. All you ever say is, 'We'll talk about it later.' I want to talk about it now. You used to have such great girls."

He has a selective memory. He had been just as irritated in the supposed good old days, whatever they were in his delusional little world. "I still do, Pete," I say casually, catching the eye of one of the mommies and flashing her a reassuring smile. Just a regular mother, here, trying to tell this guy that women don't want to have sex with him because he has such an irritating personality. "I can look at the list when I get home, but I don't have it with me right now."

"List? What list?"

Oh, God, Peter, show a *little* initiative in the brain cells department. "Just a joke," I say, lamely. How was I ever going to get this guy off the phone? "What I'm saying is that I'm out, I'm busy, and I'll be happy to talk to you later, but I can't now," I say, more firmly. Sam is throwing sand out of the sandbox. That alone is a good reason to get off the line; it's not an action destined to make me popular with anybody at the park.

"Peach, with you it's always later –"

I cut him off, ruthlessly. "Well, it is now, Peter," I say brightly. "Talk to you shortly." I press the disconnect button and sigh, carefully not looking over at the cluster of mommies. Maybe they'd believe that I'm in real estate?

Some days, that sounds like a far, far better alternative.

* * * * * *

I was going to have to make a decision about Benjamin.

After drifting casually in and out of the periphery of my life for nearly two years, he had finally decided that he needed more than a garage band and an occasional night in my apartment, which was, of course, very good indeed. Don't get me wrong about that, I just wasn't sure where, or even whether, I fit in with his new plans.

He stopped driving altogether, stopped working for the taxi company, stopped moonlighting as a driver for my service at night. He sat around my living room floor for several weeks surrounded by glossy brochures from various schools, frowning at them, muttering to himself. It would have been tremendously endearing if it hadn't made me so nervous.

While I wasn't altogether comfortable with my relationship with Benjamin, I feared losing it. What if whatever it was that he was looking for took him away from me?

So I tested him. I manufactured reasons to be angry with him. I drank and partied and ignored him for days on end, then attacked him, not listening to any kind of reason, finding myself in an insane-feeling groove where I was more invested in being angry than in fixing what was making me angry in the first place. Not the most pleasant of situations.

Benjamin put up with it all. He left when I threw things at him and came back after I had calmed down. He tinkered around the apartment, fixing things that he hadn't had the time to get to for months. He made love to me slowly and tenderly and sweetly. He kept looking at the brochures.

Finally, he made up his mind, and enrolled at the famous North Bennet Street School in Boston's Italian North End. North Bennet Street has an international reputation as a craftsman's school, one of a vanishing breed. It's been around since 1885, and the name alone commands respect. I'm not sure that there are too many names that do that anymore.

I was in awe. Here was someone I thought was going to spend the rest of his life drifting in and out of jobs, drifting in and out of bands, drifting in and out of me. Yet he was making decisions that were radically changing the course of his life.

Still, I was a little scared that once he did that, I wouldn't have a place in his life anymore.

So I was fairly delighted when he asked me to go with him and visit the school.

Here you can learn piano technology, jewelry making, locksmithing, bookbinding, violin making and restoration, and – Benjamin's choice – restoration carpentry. In an age of fast food, fast sex, fast education, North Bennet stands out as the continu- ation of a long tradition of apprenticeship in crafts that may well disappear altogether if Wal-Mart has its way.

Or so Benjamin told me. I was still trying to catch up with his enthusiasm. Ideas I didn't even know he had ever considered were tumbling out. He was going to bring back the beauty of old places. He had been looking around, he said, going on ghost hunts, looking at abandoned mills and tumbledown houses.

He wanted to bring life back into these buildings, and he wanted to do it right. He wanted to learn how.

I had underestimated him, had thought that the Mnemonic band and the Sunday afternoon football games were all that was going on in his world. I looked at the craftspeople at the North Bennet Street School, at their concentration, their joy, and their attention to detail. I looked at the answering light in Benjamin's face, and I knew that something magical was happening here. Like Jen describing the early-morning masses of her childhood, I absolutely knew that the earth was moving, that something powerful and unique was being created, called into being inside him.

When Benjamin's acceptance came through, I took him to Aquitaine in the St. Cloud building on Tremont Street to celebrate. We sat at a table with a pristine white tablecloth, drank very good wine, and ate far too much. As I looked at him over the rim of my wineglass, I had the sudden feeling that I was looking at a stranger, at someone I had never seen before.

I don't mean that in a negative way. *Au contraire*, there was a certain frisson of excitement, a feeling like I could discover him all over again. It was an exciting feeling, and I entwined my fingers in his, seeing him as though on a first date.

A couple of his eyebrow hairs grew against the others, and I found that endearing. I sat gazing into his eyes, totally unconscious of movement around us, of diners coming and going, of the wind whipping up and down Tremont outside the restaurant, just sitting and drinking and falling in love with Benjamin.

When they finally closed the doors behind us, we went back to my apartment, sitting silently in the back of the taxi, clutching each other's hands with a sort of desperation I couldn't remember ever feeling in my life before. We didn't even kiss, or touch each other, as I would have done – who am I kidding, as I *had* done – with half a dozen other men. This was eerie: it was so much more simple, intense, and frightening than groping each other could ever be.

I followed him in, closing the door behind me and leaning slightly against it. For the first time since I was a teenager, I was unsure of what to do next. Then his breath was on my neck and he was taking my hand in his. "Come with me." I went.

He made me lie on the bed while he lit candles. Usually it's my job to do that. In fact, when it comes to atmosphere, it's pretty much written in stone that if you want it, it's the woman who's going to provide it. You know I'm right.

But Benjamin was there, sliding the jazz CDs into the player, lighting candles and incense, creating the mood. Deliberate, careful, caring. When he got back to the bed his hands were gentle on me, taking off my clothes slowly and carefully, his eyes never leaving mine, as though I were somehow fragile, sacred, special. His lips were all over my body – his tongue, his hands, caressing, moving, shaping. I wanted him more than I could have imagined wanting anyone ever before.

Sometimes sex makes you forget everything, especially yourself. You get obliterated somehow in the torrent of feelings, and sometimes that's what you want.

Making love with Benjamin that night wasn't about obliteration. It wasn't about losing myself. It was about becoming myself. It was about finding something warm and intense that I had always thought was outside of me. Instead, it was deep inside, located at the core of my being, a flame, a light, a brightness that I'd been spending a lot of time looking for. In sex. In alcohol. In drugs. In love.

It took Benjamin to show me that it was there and had been from the beginning.

We made love slowly at first, then with building intensity, making something physical into something metaphysical, making something mundane into something spectacular. I was going higher than I had ever dreamed I could go.

PHONING IT IN

I'm setting up for work, and I can feel a headache building.

It's the weather. You know those people, the ones with an old injury or arthritis who can tell you when a storm's coming just from the stiffness of their joints? My headaches are like that, the most tiresome barometer in the world.

It's been a quiet afternoon. Sam had homework and I watched him do it. When he was finished we made brownies in the kitchen, laughing and getting chocolate all over each other.

Jane arrived just before six.

I love Jane. I don't know how I managed to find someone who is equally at home doing the phones, studying, or reading bedtime stories to my son, but I have, and I try to never take her for granted. She originally came to work for me as an escort in her first year of graduate school at Boston College, but her husky voice and unflappable personality had me try her out on the phones; and she never looked back.

She doesn't take any shit from the clients, but she also has such a charming way of setting limits with them that they don't ever seem to know what hit them. She can talk clients into seeing someone they had already refused to see on three other occasions, and make them thank her for it, too.

I know I'm on a short-term lease with Jane. Eventually she's going to get tired of being in school and get herself a real job, but in the meantime, she's mine. She finished her Master's last year and went directly into her PhD, so I have her for a few years more, I hope.

Sam loves her, calls her Auntie Jane, and she brings him treats – colored paper, special marking pens, or the occasional piece of fruit. She lives near a Brazilian market in Somerville, so she's always picking up things I've never heard of before.

Tonight she's here for babysitting duties. "Just get him his bath, can you?" I asked as I pressed the buttons on my cell to check my messages.

Jane was looking at me and the kitchen. I'd forgotten the chocolate. "Looks like the whole family could use one," she observed. "What was it, a lab experiment?"

"Where I come from," I said, the phone pressed to my ear, "we call this cooking."

She raised her eyebrows but didn't say anything. Sam burst into the room. "It smells like they're ready, Mom!" Sam doesn't believe in saying anything that can be shouted instead. I winced.

"Hi, Aunt Jane!"

"Hi, yourself, Sam," she said easily. "What's going on in the kitchen?"

"Brownies!"

"Cool. Can I come see?"

"Yeah." He looked back at me. "You coming, too, Mom?"

I shook my head. "Have to work tonight, honey," I said, feeling a real tug of regret as I did. Every working mother's lament – there's just not enough time to do it all. When Sam was small and wasn't in school, my working nights didn't matter as much: we had our days together, and he was by and large asleep before my own workday got into full swing. But school gets out at three, and that's not a lot of time to be together.

Sam was philosophical about it. "Come on, then," he said to Jane with a shrug and a peremptory tug on her hand. "You can tell me when they're coming out!"

I went into my office and closed the door softly behind me, my family on the other side and my heart rebelling. As I said, every working mother's conflict.

My office isn't particularly officelike. I don't work from my bed, as I did in my single, childless days, but this is as close to a boudoir as I can get and still have it on the first floor of the house. A sofa so wide two people can lie on it comfortably together (I know – we've done it), piled high with cushions that I position around me for comfort – or fling at the wall when I need to release some tension. The requisite pile of paperback books, the requisite television and remote control, all easily within reach.

I used to work with a bottle of wine nearby; now it's spring water. I'm getting healthier as I get older.

That's not such a bad thing.

I had a pretty good idea of who was going to be available, so I made the calls swiftly. "Jenny? You around tonight? Great, you should be hearing from me shortly." I lit a cigarette and opened one of the paperbacks, and scrawled Jenny's name on the inside front cover. I can tell which nights were which, according to what I was reading that evening.

The phone had already started ringing before my list was complete. "Peach? Who's on tonight?"

"Hi, Evan. I've got Tina. You've seen her before. Does that work for you?"

"Sure. Have her give me a call."

I disconnect, breathing a prayer of thanks for people like Evan. Every time he calls, he sees whomever I suggest. Manna from heaven, that's what a client like Evan is.

It doesn't stay that good, of course. It never does. By nine I've slipped out to kiss Sam good night, opened a new pack of cigarettes, and nearly finished my first gallon of spring water. And I have Roger on the line. "I really want to see Amy, Peach; can you set that up?"

"I can try," I say, cautiously. The aforementioned Amy isn't exactly my steadiest and most reliable employee. She's also drop-dead gorgeous and *everybody* wants to see her, all the time. "Give me a half-hour and I'll get back to you."

I take a deep breath. Roger's a good client – doesn't give me a hard time, sees someone from my service two or three times a month like clockwork, never hassles about time or money. Sometimes he even lets me schedule him in advance, something pretty much unheard of in my line of work, where impulse buys are more the norm. I punch in Amy's number and she answers on the seventh ring.

"Hey, it's Peach; I've got work if you want it."

She giggles. I truly hope that she's either watching TV or has somebody there – when people start giggling by themselves it's a bad sign. "Hi, Peach."

It's unclear whether she's been drinking, doing drugs, both, or neither. But I really want her to see Roger. "Can you do a call?" I ask, making my voice even and – though it's an effort – cheerful.

There's a pause. "Sure, Peach. Who?"

"Roger Jones. Over in West Roxbury. You've seen him before." I take a hurried breath and continue before she has a chance to voice an objection. "His number is 555-6676. Give him a call right now, and call me back, okay?"

"What was that number?"

I repeat it. "Call me right back, honey."

"Okay, Peach."

I send out two more quick calls, one to the Sheraton downtown, one to the mentally retarded client in Medford, and then the phone rings again. "Hey, Peach, sorry to bother you, it's Roger. No luck with Amy?"

I'm not about to explode all over Roger. "She should be calling you very shortly," I assure him, keeping my voice warm and calm. "I think she was just rearranging her plans so she can see you. I know that she likes you; maybe it's taking a little longer than she thought."

"Oh, okay, great. I'll wait, then."

I picture him in his small neat house on Lagrange Street next to the cemetery. The house is empty, way too empty, since Roger's wife died of cancer two years ago. He doesn't bother to date; I'm not sure that he's even interested in remarrying. One of the girls told me that his mantelpiece is like a shrine to his wife. I know he's sitting there now, just sitting, maybe with the evening news on the television, maybe not. He'll have nothing scheduled for tonight, nothing but the thought of Amy coming, giggling and bright and young and carefree, to make him feel even remotely better about his life. I grit my teeth.

Amy …

She doesn't answer her phone, which is not a good sign. I try her cell. Also not happening. It's after seven. I glance at the list of names I scrawled in the margin of page five of the Eudora Welty. Karen. Karen might work. She's not as effervescent as Amy, but she's young, cute, and impervious to others' moods. Some people call that insensitivity. I call it the potential for longevity.

"Hey, Karen, it's Peach. Got work for you."

"Hi, Peach." She sounds breathless; she's probably on her treadmill. Every time I call her, she's on her treadmill. I've never known anyone so much in love with one. "What time?"

"As soon as you can get there. Roger Jones, in West Roxbury."

"Shit. My car's in the shop."

That would have been good information to have when you signed on an hour and a half ago, I think sourly. "Okay, I'll get you a driver."

"I hate using drivers." A pause and a glugging sound as she downs some water. I can feel the pounding on the treadmill coming over the phone line.

"They end up costing me. Can't you find me a guy who lives on the T?"

Yeah, I'm the original miracle maker. "Karen, it would help me out a lot if you'd see him. He's a good client, he's really easy." I allow a bit of doubt to creep into my voice. "It's looking like a slow night, I'm not sure I'll have anything else for you." That usually gets a little action, a bit more of a positive response. Usually.

Karen's playing prima donna. "Why don't we wait and see if something else comes in, and then, if it doesn't, I'll go see this Roger guy," she says.

Who is in charge here, anyway? "I'm sending someone to him now," I say. "I'll see if there's anything for you later." I press the disconnect button before she can respond. Damn, damn, damn.

I call Roger. "Hey, it's Peach. I think that Amy might have a class tonight, I can't reach her. I have a couple of really sweet girls, you've never met either of them, but would you be interested? I honestly can't commit to getting in touch with Amy, after all."

"Can you tell me about the other girls?"

"Well, I have Zoë. She's a student, too. I think she's studying to be an elementary school teacher." A lot of the clients like that, someone gentle and sweet. "She's five feet six inches, 125 pounds, 36-26-34. She has long hair. She's really pretty." I pause, but there's no response from Roger; he's waiting for the menu recitation to be complete. Some nights, that's exactly how I feel: "Hi, I'm Peach, and I'll be your waitress tonight. We have some specials I'd like to tell you about."

I shake my head to clear it and forge on. "There's also a really gorgeous blonde, she's twenty-three, her name is Sara. She's five-foot-seven, 120 pounds, 38-26-34. What do you think?"

Roger's such a – well, honestly, such a peach, no pun intended. "Whatever you think, I guess. You know me. I'd just like to see somebody soon." A picture of him flashes across my mind again, his long lonely evening stretching out in front of him, the empty voices from the cemetery mocking his solitude. I really want to throttle both Amy and Karen at this point. "Give me a few minutes," I say. "I'll see what I can do for you."

We're just about two hours into the Roger saga now, and in the meantime, the phone hasn't stopped ringing. I send someone out to see Peter Povaklas. I call the girl out from the Sheraton and arrange for the driver to meet her and pick up her fee; she's relatively new, and I don't like girls holding a lot of money for me when I don't know them yet. I call Zoë/Kim, which is how I generally think of girls when they're using another escort name. "Work," I say, economically. Third time's the charm, right? "Roger Jones, West Roxbury, his number is 555-6676. Give him a call and call me right back and let me know."

I disconnect before she has a chance to argue, something which everybody tonight seems in the mood to do. What happened, did the planets move into some negative alignment, or something?

Zoë/Kim calls back ten minutes later. "I'm all set, Peach, I'll call you when I get there."

Oh, my God, something went right. I sigh in relief. "Thanks, honey. Talk to you then."

Peter Povaklas calls to complain. He had "ordered," as he so elegantly put it, a girl to stay for two hours. He wants her to stay for a third, and she doesn't want to. "Put her on the phone," I say.

"Hey, Peach." I can hear the weariness in her voice. I'd be pretty weary, too, after two hours with Peter.

"Hi, honey. You don't want to do another hour?" As much sympathy as I feel for her, I'd love for her to stay. I get my fee for each and every hour someone stays with the client, with no extra work. It's sweet for both me and the girl, usually, another full hour's money without more telephoning, traveling, all that sort of thing.

"No." There's an edge to her voice. I can understand that, too. "I – um – I told Peter already, I have an audition in the morning, I have to get enough sleep." Whether or not she actually does have an audition is moot; she clearly wants to get out of there. So we won't get the extra hour. I give in. "Okay, that's fine, honey, put Peter back on."

"So?" He's always belligerent off the bat.

I take a moment to light a cigarette, just to show him who's in control here. I imagine him tapping his toe as I go through the initial inhale and exhale. Damn, but that tastes good. "So she has an audition and can't stay, Peter. I can't force her. That's not the way I run my business. Do you want me to try and get someone else over there to see you?"

"I want her to stay." Now he sounds like my kid. No, I take that back: Sam never sounds quite that petulant. If he did, it would be the last time he tried it.

It's not the first time that I realize that running an escort service is great training for parenthood.

"I know, Pete, but she can't. When I send someone over there, I only guarantee the time we agree on. I can't make anybody stay if they don't want to."

He clearly doesn't understand why someone wouldn't want to. "I gave her a glass of wine," he says, sulkily, as though this unprecedented act of generosity should buy him her allegiance forever.

"I'm sure she enjoyed it," I say. There's another call coming in. "Okay, Pete, I have to go. Is she on her way out?"

"She's getting dressed. Already." He's going to make it hard for her to get out of there, I can tell.

"Fine. Ask her to call me from her cell phone when she's in her car, will you? As soon as she gets out? I need to talk to her." This way, he knows that if she doesn't call me, I'll be calling him. A not-so-subtle reminder. It's hard to be subtle with Pete. "And – do you want to see another girl tonight?"

"I'll think about it."

"You do that." I press buttons and just miss the incoming call. Caller ID proclaims it to be a number I don't know, and I don't have the energy to pursue it. I'll pick up the voice mail in a minute. There's some sort of altercation taking place on the television, and I consider for a moment putting the volume on and seeing what it's all about. Frankly, anyone else's soap opera sounds pretty good to me at this point – misery loves company more than you know – but I decide instead to take a break and head to the kitchen for an iced coffee. Enough of this healthy shit.

Jane is at the kitchen table, her laptop and textbooks open all around her, having an argument with her boyfriend on her cell phone. She waves to me as I pass. "That's ridiculous," she is saying. "I never told him anything of the sort." I pour the coffee and lean against the sink, sipping slowly. Sometimes it helps just to get out of the office. "Call me back later, Brian," says Jane. "When you feel like telling me the truth."

I sip my coffee and don't say anything. She shakes her head. "I hate men," she intones, darkly.

"I know that feeling," I agree and head back to the office.

I send Sara out to a two-hour call up on the North Shore and the phone rings again. "Hey, Peach, it's Roger. Sorry to bother you ..."

Hell. I look at the clock. Zoë/Kim should have been there twenty minutes ago. I just assumed she forgot to check in. Some of the girls who have worked for other services don't; they watch their own time. Whatever works. "Hi, Roger," I say, cautiously.

"Hey. Um, I was just wondering, Zoë said she'd be here by now ..."

"Yes," I agree. "She should be. Let me get a hold of her and find out what's happening, and I'll call you right back."

"Okay."

Holy shit. I page Zoë/Kim and punch in an extra 911 to my phone number for emphasis.

Jane's at the door. "Hey, Sam's asleep, you need me to stay?"

"No. Thanks, honey."

She frowned. "You okay?"

"Just the usual," I shrug. "Peter Povaklas, and girls are disappearing. You don't want to know."

"You're so right. I don't." She blows me a kiss and closes the door behind her. We're always careful about that, closing the door. Sam thinks that I do telemarketing for a living. He knows that it's perfectly fine to knock on the office door at night, and he does, but I don't ever leave it open, just in case.

181

The phone rings: a new client. I'm polite, but he doesn't want to leave his real name and that doesn't fly. I don't ask for much. "Perhaps you can call back next week," I say, insincerely, and am disconnecting just as Amy's number reappears on the radar. "Hey, Peach, sorry, got busy. Do you want me to see anyone?"

Do I? Only about three hours ago, I did. I take a deep breath. I have no idea where Zoë/Kim is, but I'm not messing up Roger's life any more than I have to. "I do if you can get yourself over to West Roxbury now. And I mean *now*."

She is cheerfulness itself. "Roger? Sure. Tell him I'm on my way."

"Are you really on your way? I'm not jerking this guy around."

"Of course I am, Peach!" She sounds genuinely surprised. "Why wouldn't I be?"

I bite back several potential answers and disconnect. I page Zoë/Kim again, and call Roger. "Great news, Amy's on her way!"

"Okay," he sounds bemused. "Seriously, you know, if it's a problem, I can call again another day." He's probably thinking longingly of bed – and sleep – at this point. I know I am.

"No, Roger, I really apologize. It's just been a really crazy night. You've been very patient and I can't say how much I appreciate it."

Ten minutes later, Amy checks in. She's actually at Roger's house and everything is fine. I feel like I've run a marathon. Sometimes I get my fee easily, adding an hour on to something that's already been booked, that sort of thing. But nights like tonight, I've sometimes had to make up to eighteen or twenty phone calls to send one girl on one call. It's not always easy.

I page Zoë/Kim and put out another call. The coffee kicks in and I feel pretty good; it is also starting to look like an early night, which is definitely good news.

I never put out late-night calls. I'm talking three, four in the morning. Those are the creepy ones, the ones that are hard to screen, the ones where drug use is pretty much guaranteed. People who suddenly decide at four o'clock in the morning that they need to see an escort have needs that I don't even want to know about. You don't just suddenly decide that. There's something else going on.

I can't imagine ever being so poor I'd take those risks, either for myself or my girls. If I need extra money, these days, I just turn the phones on earlier, send girls out in the afternoons. A lot of the married clients like that, either at their place or at some hotel. Gets everything taken care of and you're still home for supper at six.

Usually if I'm still going late, it's just to call someone out, someone who's been on a superlong call, something like that. That's it. I'm usually in bed before two; midnight is more usual, giving me enough sleep to face Sam and breakfast and all that sort of thing. His dad helps out, but he's usually off on a job earlier in the morning than I even want to think about. We've made it work.

Things are winding down; I'm finishing up what I promise myself will be my last pack of cigarettes tonight. A client calls and books someone for next Tuesday, which is odd, but fine. People don't generally book that far in advance. It's an immediate gratification sort of thing, this industry. But, as I said, fine.

Zoë/Kim finally calls back around midnight. She got lost, then stopped for directions and met a friend and, well, one thing led to another and … "Never mind," I say, wearily. What probably happened was that she met up with someone that she turned into an extracurricular call of her own.

I'm fine with that. As long as girls don't steal my clients, they can work for other services, they can have private clients, whatever. But in this case, she might have had the courtesy to let me know she wasn't going to make it to West Roxbury.

Courtesy. Hmm, now there's a concept. As I've said before, I'm not usually working with people who have their shit together. Why should I expect her to be different?

I don't care. It's one o'clock, and I turn off the phones, turn off the television, turn off the lights.

ADDICTION

Clients don't use nearly as many drugs now as they did – even ten years ago, much less when I started the business.

Back then, it was all coke, and everyone did it. *I* did it, and often to excess, so this isn't about throwing stones while living in a glass house. It's about addiction, which is rampant in the world I live and work in.

There are sexual addiction issues, too – what a surprise. I have clients who call me every night, sometimes two or three times a night. They can't afford to see someone that frequently, but the contact with the service works for them as a temporary fix.

I try to discourage this, of course. There are always guys who will try to use me as an aural substitute for the real thing: "So tell me again what she looks like … hmmm … What size breasts? Yeah? What shape are they, really round? Uhhh …" Yuck.

Sometimes I feed into it, just a little, if I think that it's going to lead to a call; but these are the guys I really hate to hear on the other end of the line. This is not a sex chatline.

Some of them are even aware of the problem. Jack Wilson is one. He was seeing girls two and three times a week, sometimes for two hours at a time, sometimes two girls at a time. When he realized that the spending was getting out of control, he went into therapy.

I got a call about a week later.

"Hello, Peach? This is – um – Jack."

"Hi, Jack," I said cheerfully. Jack means money.

"Yeah. Well. Listen, I have to ask you something. For a favor, actually, I have to ask you for a favor."

"Sure," I said easily. "What can I do for you?"

There was a long silence on the other end of the line. I began to wonder if we'd been disconnected. "Jack? Are you there?"

"Um, yeah. I'm here. This is – oh, gee, this is a little embarrassing."

I raised my eyebrows, though of course he couldn't see me. When you consider the really, really strange requests that I get on a regular basis, you have to wonder what on earth a client could find embarrassing. There's plenty of stuff that goes on in my little world that *I* find embarrassing, mind you, but my clients are cheerfully unaware of my reactions to some of their preferences. "Don't worry, Jack," I said, encouragingly.

"I'm fine with you telling me anything." As long as it's not little girls or animals, that is.

"Okay. Okay, well, here goes. I – um – I want you to cut me off."

I blinked. "Cut you off?" I repeated.

"Yeah. I mean – you know – I'm trying not to do this so much. The sex thing, you know." Yeah, well, Jack, I didn't think you were talking about excess carbohydrates. "I mean, I can't afford it, not really, and my shrink says I need to stop. Well, at least ease off some. And I know he's right, you know? I know it's kind of taken control of my life." He coughed, or at least pretended to. "So anyway, here's the thing, I'm not sure I'm going to be all that good at this. In fact, I'm pretty sure that I'm not." Another hesitation. "Cause I really don't want to give it up, you know? But I know I have to. I know that's what's good for me. So anyway, Peach, what I'm saying is that I'm going to keep calling you, probably, and I want you to not send me anybody."

Whoa, Nellie. You want to call me and tell me that you want me to make some good money, and then I'm supposed to tell you, oh, gee, no, Jack, but thanks anyway? Do I look like a moron to you? I gritted my teeth.

On the other hand, Jack had been a really good client for over three years. We had talked almost daily during that time. He was as close to a colleague as I was ever likely to get, in the sense that we "worked" together so much and so often – and he was in trouble. He was asking me for help. I took a deep breath and tried not to think about my bank account. "Jack, let me understand. I'm supposed to say no when you call next to ask for a call."

"Um … yes."

"Okay, I'll do it." I was a little hesitant. "How often do you anticipate this happening?"

"Probably every day." Here was a guy, at any rate, who was willing to look squarely at himself in the mirror. "I'm serious. I want you – no, that's not it, damn it, I *need* you – to refuse to send me someone." His breathing was a little ragged. "Christ, I don't want to be doing this, Peach."

"I know," I said, automatically reassuring him. "I know you don't. And I'll help."

"You mean that?" He was pathetically relieved.

"Of course I do." But I wasn't so sure.

It didn't take long for our mutual resolve to be put to the test. The following Saturday was insane – people were crawling out of the woodwork – and in the middle of it all Jack called. "Hi, Peach." He sounded like a little boy unsure of his welcome. As well he might.

"Hi, Jack," I said. "What's up?"

"Well, I was wondering who's on tonight," he said, his carefully casual voice not totally obliterating the quaver beneath, like someone writing and presenting a check that they know is going to bounce.

"Jack," I said, "I can't talk to you tonight. It's really busy here."

There was a slight pause. "Okay, okay. I know what you're doing," he said.

"I'm glad you do," I said. "Gotta go."

"Wait!" It was a yelp. "Don't hang up! You know that thing we talked about last week?" There was a slight pause, then he hurried on as if afraid of what I might say. "You know, so, okay, I was thinking about it. And I'm going to start that program, I really am, real soon. I'm committed, you know? But I decided, um, you know, just to taper down a little first. I don't think I can handle it cold turkey. I have a much better chance of success if I do it slowly."

And I don't have time for your bullshit, I thought silently. "Jack, that's not what you said before."

"I know." Some animosity had crept into his tone. "I know, but I've changed my mind. I want to see someone tonight."

I groaned. "Hold on." I switched to the other line. "Hello?"

"Hey, Peach, it's Gary."

"Hold on a minute," I told him. I switched back to the first line. "Jack, I have to go."

"No!" He was belligerent and panicked all at once. "I want to see someone!"

"Sorry, Jack." I disconnected and got back to work. He called again within five minutes. "Peach, look, I don't care what I said before. I want to see someone tonight."

I balanced the telephone between my ear and my shoulder while I lit a cigarette, giving me a moment to think. "We don't have anyone you'd like," I said, trying another tack.

"I don't believe you. You said you were so busy just a few minutes ago. Who's on?"

I sighed. I'm all for being cooperative, but this was ridiculous. It's bad enough having to play these stupid games when I get paid at the end of the night, but here I was playing the game and doing it for no money at all. This does not compute. "Jack, I'm trying to be helpful to you here. You asked me to shut you off. I am. I'm also very busy. Please leave me alone."

"I'll call another service!"

"You do that." That was just fine with me: the perfect solution, in fact. I got to do what was right and not have to argue with someone pestering me for sex all night.

The bad thing was I knew he wouldn't follow through on his threat. Some clients are sluts and call every service in town, playing one off against the other. Some are monogamous. Jack, fortunately or unfortunately, fit into the latter category.

Sure enough, within a half hour he was back on the line. I recognized the number on my caller ID and was ready for him. "Jack, stop calling me. I really can't talk to you tonight."

"I have the money right here. I want to see someone. Now."

"I don't have anyone for you." How long was I supposed to be virtuous, anyway? I pictured the crisp hundred-dollar bills in his hand and banished the thought immediately. I was supposed to be helping him. "Listen, Jack, if you still feel the same way tomorrow, call me then, and I'll hook you up, okay? But at least sleep on it."

As if an addict has ever been able to just sleep off that kind of insistent need. I can still remember calling the coke dealer at eight in the morning because I'd run out and wasn't able to just go to bed, as I was so self-righteously expecting Jack to do. I'm not proud of the memory, but that doesn't make it any less real.

"I'm never going to be able to sleep now!" he wailed.

They really need a rehab facility for sex addicts.

In the years that I've been in the business, I've seen a few guys like Jack, who struggled with their addictions, and a whole lot of other guys who rationalized themselves into the poorhouse by seeing it as macho and cool.

All other addictions are the same. Maybe there are more fragile people, more damaged people in my line of work, but whatever the reason, there aren't a whole lot of them, workers or clients, who are all that healthy. The ones who are, get out.

The ones who are still there, year after year, aren't the ones who are winning any awards for mental health.

The cocaine use has decreased over the years. I stopped doing it before my clients did, as I went through changes in my personal life; but I'm seeing less and less of it these days. Ten years ago, I'd say at least half of my clients were using it recreationally, and some of them a lot more heavily than that. Girls had to deal with clients who were totally railed, paranoid, jumpy, and sometimes downright scary. Those were the days when a girl could spend a third of her time with a client checking the doors and the windows for imaginary people lurking behind them. That doesn't happen very much anymore. It's now the exception rather than the rule.

They're a lot less likely these days to want to get the girls fucked up, too. Oh, I'm not saying that everyone is sweet and kind, but there's less thrill these days in messing someone else up. Or maybe they're just more cautious.

I used to have one client who, thank God, got married and dropped out. He used to be big into pills and champagne, and he didn't want to partake alone. He used to get a room in one of the smaller nondescript business hotels over on Soldiers Field Road and have three girls over, one after the other, and he expected them all to drink his champagne and take his pills.

After I got hip to what he was doing, I became more careful. All I needed was someone overdosing on her way home from a call. I told the girls to palm the pills, to fake taking them, or at least to take a taxi home after the call. That could be really difficult since many of the girls were young and not particularly practiced in the art of deception. A lot of them were into pleasing the client. A lot were curious enough to try the free drugs. As if there was such a thing as free drugs. So it was a relief when he quit.

I know that a lot of people are currently doing Ecstasy, and heroin is coming back, though we see a lot more of the former in the business. There's something about shooting up when you're on a so-called date that can be a real turn-off. And Ecstasy is supposed to make you feel loving, after all. The pharmaceuticals are coming back into their own, too – Valium, Oxycontin, Percocet, all that happy little group.

Not for me. Those days are over, and I'm grateful that I survived them. I wouldn't go back for all the cocaine in Colombia.

ALLA

I talk a lot about the problems: the girls who get lost, whether through drugs, greed, or meeting the wrong guy. I really should talk some about the lighter side of my business, because there are a lot of girls who are healthy and smart, who work and move on. Being a callgirl is not necessarily a recipe for disaster.

Most of those who work for me are students. College students, graduate students, foreign exchange students. It's the way I set things up and the decision has proven to be the correct one. My service has a certain cachet.

On the other hand, it does present certain problems. No one can work during finals week, for example. And then there's the whole roommate situation.

The way things work, I speak with the client and get him to agree to see someone. Technically, that should be that, but it never is. The girl calls the client, theoretically to confirm, and he generally plays a game or two. "Well, I'm not sure, can you describe yourself?" Even though I've already described her, I think there's a secondary thrill in talking about it so much. So even though I've already convinced him, now she has to convince him, too. Often this part of the conversation is explicit – painfully explicit. It's annoying, but an integral part of the process.

However, it is a part of the process that is absolutely impossible to manage in a college dorm with an unsuspecting roommate sitting a mere few feet away. Not something that you can come up with a snappy explanation for on the spur of the moment.

These days, most girls have cell phones, and mobility has made this transaction a lot easier. Not for everybody, however.

Alla was Russian. There is a significant Russian population in Boston, many of them Jews who came to the United States to flee all sorts of problems in the former Soviet Union, from discrimination to outright pogroms. Another generation since then has come for the same reason that so many young people come to Boston – for school. Recent immigrants, of both the legal and the illegal variety, need to work.

When they're young and beautiful, they work for me.

Alla, however, lived with her parents. The money she made as an escort went into a savings account. She was going to be prepared when she graduated with her M.B.A. and opened her own business. But in the meantime she lived at home, and her father *always* answered the phone.

I had become her friend, Catherine. Catherine and Alla apparently studied together quite a lot, especially in the evenings. Once he asked me – in such heavily accented English that I could barely understand what he was saying – what classes we were in together, and I said something vague about contracts and start-ups, which he in turn probably didn't understand either. As far as I was concerned, our level of communication was just fine.

I wouldn't have jumped through so many hoops if Alla hadn't been so profitable. She wasn't particularly pleasant to the guys she saw. In fact, she had this cold, haughty air that certainly wouldn't make me want to sleep with her. But then again, I haven't got that much in common with my clients. They certainly couldn't get enough of her. "Is Alla working tonight?" was the first thing out of a whole lot of people for a good year-and-a-half running.

She didn't have a car. And not only did she require a driver, but a driver who didn't mind taking her on side errands for no extra compensation that I could see. But I didn't ask too many questions. It was inconvenient for me, though. Instead of dropping Alla off after a call and being available to drive someone else to a call, a driver could end up spending all sorts of extra time doing Alla's bidding.

If a client even looked at her the wrong way, she'd refuse to see him again – or else would see him and require a surcharge, which, to my utter astonishment, most of them paid without a peep. And remember, these are guys who complain about *everything*. But not about Alla.

I liked to book her in advance when possible, to avoid the Cerberus that she lived with at home. Or is it the Sphinx, with its endless riddles? Perhaps this is a more appropriate mythological analogy for my relationship with Alla's father. Whatever it was, when I could escape the grilling, I was happy to do so.

She was usually amenable to scheduling in advance, not that that meant anything. Prearranged calls are not seen as written in stone, I have found, by either the client or the girl – but especially not by the girl. Sometimes Alla showed up for prescheduled calls, sometimes she didn't. She never apologized – she just took her automatic forgiveness and acceptance for granted.

Whenever that grated on my nerves, I reminded myself how much money Alla was bringing in and bit my tongue. I can be as acerbic as the best of them, but I'm not stupid.

She quit without bothering to tell me. It was the client who casually mentioned that he wouldn't be using the service anymore; he was marrying Alla.

I *did* mention that a lot of them are masochists, didn't I?

THE ROAD TO HAPPINESS

So who, exactly, are my clients?

Clients are the proverbial Everyman. They come in all shapes and sizes, all rungs on the economic ladder, all personality types.

What they are, mostly, is lonely.

I have clients, and had clients from day one, who will just call me and ask, "What's going on?" They don't want a call; they don't even necessarily get the voyeuristic thrill of finding out who is working and what they look like. Mostly, they just want to talk to me.

I used to find that amazing, that there are guys so lonely out there that they think of their service providers as their friends. That when they need to talk to somebody, they don't have anybody else to call but somebody who makes money off their loneliness. I remember an episode of *Frasier* when Niles, newly separated from Maris, is struggling (for about the hundredth time) with whether or not to tell Daphne about his feelings for her.

"So," Niles is saying on the telephone, "you think that I should go ahead and tell her? Yes, yes, that makes sense. Thanks for your advice."

He is interrupted by the doorbell.

"Oh, I have to go," Niles says into the phone. "So, okay, that'll be a one-year subscription, and I'll take the travel alarm clock."

I remember watching that episode with my mouth hanging open. Niles was just like one of my clients, I thought, asking me – a person who is in his life on a purely commercial basis – for advice, expecting me to provide caring and support in times of need and indecision.

I used to think that was pathetic. Long ago, I even used to laugh at these people.

Now? Well, I've gotten a lot more empathetic. The Dalai Lama says that the true route to happiness is through compassion – and life is proving him right, as it has a tendency to do. I may have mourned not having grown up Catholic, but if I have any faith and practice at all in my life now, it's Buddhist. The route to happiness is through compassion. It's through feeling what the other person is feeling, and knowing, with absolute certainty and conviction, that it's really only a quirk of fate that he's in his shoes and you're in yours.

I'm not sure that my mother ever saw it like that. If she ever empathized with anybody, she wouldn't have been able to express it in any way, certainly not in her circles, but I learnt something. Just because I'm on this end of the phone and they're on the other doesn't mean that I am any better, smarter, or more together than any of my clients.

They may be messed up now, but I've been pretty messed up myself, so who is to say if either of us has it more together than the other?

We're all the same, in the end. The road to happiness is through compassion, and that's where my faith is these days, in knowing that any of us can fail, or fall, at any time. And even when we don't, we're surely no better than those who have.

* * * * * *

I was in a gallery on Newbury Street looking at some Asian artwork when I turned a corner and saw a Ming vase. Suddenly, all I could smell was furniture polish. There was something there, something I couldn't quite remember, a tip-of-the-tongue feeling. Ming vases and furniture polish – and then I had it.

Standing in the hallway of my parents' house on South Battery Street, next to a table, smelling the furniture polish. The housekeeper must have just cleaned that morning. Smelling that furniture polish and listening to muffled voices talking inside the room. My father dying.

My father dying, and asking for me. I had that to hold onto – but there was more. I narrowed my eyes, looking at the vase. There was something about it …

I was standing in the hallway and the others had left, the doctor still talking to my mother in low, concerned tones, the two men in business suits following in their wake, grown-ups as usual taking no more notice of me.

The bedroom door was shut. I wanted to go in, I could feel it as though it were happening now, that closed door tugging at my heart, pulling me toward it … I took a step, my hand going to the knob – it was glass, the knob was made of glass, and as I touched it, my mother's voice: "Abby! Come down here!"

I pulled my hand back as quickly as if it had been burned. "Yes, ma'am," I called. I didn't move.

"Abby! Did you hear me, child? I mean *now*!"

I stood in the hallway, indecisive, looking at the door. Daddy was in there, and if I opened the door, he would want to see me. If I opened it, I wouldn't have to be brave anymore, I could cry and cry and cry and Daddy wouldn't mind, because he was just as sad about dying and leaving me as I was about him, I just knew it. Daddy wouldn't mind that they had told me not to go; Daddy would tell –

"Abigail!"

"Yes, ma'am!" I shrieked, turning away from the door one last time. The vase was sitting on the table, priceless, important. Things, I had been taught, were very important.

With all of my strength, I picked up the vase and hurled it to the floor.

THE MOST IMPORTANT PERSON

After I had been in business for almost ten years, I was asking myself questions about the future. Well, not about the future as a generality, but my future.

I was popular. I was wellknown. An article about me had appeared in *Boston Magazine*. Not about me as Abby, of course: that was my secret. The articles were about me as Peach, everything was about me as Peach.

Bartenders in the hottest clubs knew me by name. I was making good money, I was independent, I was happy. Or rather, I should have been happy.

Benjamin wasn't happy, and was making that very clear.

"Hey, Abby, I'm thinking about going into business with this guy at school, when we graduate, I mean. Open a business out in California."

California. My stomach contracted in panic. "Why not here?"

He shrugged. "He's from out there, and there's a lot of work. Victorians in San Francisco, you know, stuff like that."

Frightened, my initial reaction was to become difficult, prim. I'm revolting when I go into lecture mode, and I only do it when I'm scared. "That doesn't make sense. There's a lot more restoration work to do in the East. There have been buildings here a lot longer."

He hardly spared me a glance. We were eating brunch at the Swisshotel at Lafayette Place and he had the newspaper open next to his croissant and freshly squeezed orange juice. He was paying it as much attention as he was me. "I don't know why, but the work is there," he said, briefly, his eyes scanning the headlines. "This guy has a lot of contacts, too, somewhere near Morro Bay."

I was twisting my napkin in my lap. "So what about me?"

He folded the paper with deliberation, took a sip of coffee, and sat back before he finally looked at me. "What do you mean?"

"What about me? What about us?" I was dangerously close to whining.

Benjamin appeared to think about it for a moment. "I'm not so sure there is an *us*, Abby," he said, finally. "It's you, and me when you want me to be there. That was fine for a while, that was a lot of fun, don't get me wrong. But I'm ready to grow up now."

"What are you talking about?" I knew exactly what he was talking about. "You're the one who's always decided when to come and go. You're the one who won't move in with me."

He smiled, but there wasn't a lot of warmth in the smile. "I've made decisions inside the parameters you've left me," he said. "Face it, Abby: you want me around when the others aren't there. When your apartment isn't full of people admiring you. When you're sad and lonely and hung over, that's when you want me. The rest of the time, Sid and Court are company enough for you. The rest of the time, you have more important people to spend your time with."

"That isn't true! There's no one more important than you!" I hadn't known it, not really, until that moment.

"Then prove it." His voice was cool, detached. He could have been discussing one of the headlines in the newspaper.

"How?" My hackles went up again. "I'm not moving to California with you!"

He glanced around, quickly, and I realized that my voice was getting louder, strident, maybe even a little out of control; people were looking at us. "I'm sorry," I said more quietly, not contrite at all. "But you can't expect me to move to —"

"I don't." There was a smile playing with the corners of his mouth. "I'm not so sure I want to go there myself."

"So you were just saying that to get me going." I was huffing and puffing again.

"No." He leaned across the table and put his hand on top of mine. "Stop it, Abby. Slow down." He didn't move his hand, even though I tried to tug mine away. "Just listen, for once, okay? I love you but I don't love our life together. I need to know that it's not always going to be like this, and I'm not sure that's something you can guarantee. I think you like things the way they are, and that's a problem for me."

I was still stuck on the first part of his monologue. "You love me?"

The smile became real and warm. "Yeah. I love you."

"Oh." I wasn't trying to move my hand anymore. This was nice. So maybe I'm way too romantic at heart, especially for someone in my profession, but this was still really nice.

Benjamin wasn't finished. "But I can't see us in the future –"

I hesitated, and looked at him. "You really love me?" I knew what the answer was, but I needed to hear it, again and again if necessary.

He seemed nonplussed. "Of course I love you, Abby."

We stayed like that for a moment, close, feeling each other's breath. He smelled of buttered toast and coffee. It was an enormously comforting smell. "Okay," I said, softly.

"Okay, what?"

"Okay. Whatever you want." I hesitated. "What exactly is it that you want?" I smiled, seeing the humor in the situation.

He grinned, the release of tension palpable between us. "Well, I do happen to have a list ..."

I cuffed him, playfully. "No list. What do you want?"

He leaned back. He was enjoying this. "World peace. Season tickets to the Red Sox for the rest of my life, or better still, for them to finally win a frigging *championship* ..."

"Aha. I knew you were a Boston boy."

"Yeah, well ..." He touched my hand again, stroking it, watching what he was doing, then abruptly looked up at me. "I want to be the most important person in your life," he said, softly.

"You are." I hadn't known it before, but I was telling the truth as I said it.

"And I want us to live together. Not just me moving into your place – finding a place of our own. Something that is ours."

I loved my apartment in Bay Village, loved the skylight and the exposed brick and the bathroom that was the size of a master bedroom. I took a deep breath. "Okay."

"And I want us to be together. To make plans together, plans for the future. To be a couple."

"Okay."

"That's it? You mean it?"

I smiled. "Yeah. I mean it."

"Okay, then."

It wasn't exactly Shakespeare, or the most passionate declaration of love and intent ever made, but it sure rocked my world. Within a week we started looking at apartments. Within a month we found one. It was a townhouse in Charlestown, recently refurbished, on a quiet cobbled street. Not far from Olive's, arguably one of Boston's best restaurants, or so I babbled to anyone who asked me about the move. As if I had to convince them that I was still staying hip even if I was leaving Bay Village. In truth it was me I was trying to convince, but it wasn't a difficult thing to do. Staying hip was becoming more meaningless all the time.

I think it started, really, when Jenny stopped working for me. Not that her decision carried that much weight in my life, but it reminded me, somehow, that others were moving on and I was standing still. She stopped being an escort, stopped teaching, started writing full-time, and got married to someone who had nothing to do with the world we had shared. She sounded happy, really happy; there was a lightness in her voice I hadn't heard before. Her migraines had gone away. She was laughing more than she used to; and I wanted to laugh more, too.

My mother was bemused. "Charlestown?" she asked, pointedly, and I couldn't fail to see the irony of the name and its approximation to Charleston. "Just being consistent," I told her, lightly, and went out to buy curtains. We hired movers who came and took my things away from the brownstone in the Bay Village and I saw the tenants from the floors below me peeking out as my furniture was trundled by their doors. How curious – I'd lived here for years and, true to city life, had never exchanged more than a few words in passing with any of them. Then again, perhaps I hadn't wanted to.

I sat on the big stone steps and leaned against the black ironwork of the banister and realized that I had no idea what any of my neighbors had thought of me while I lived there. Much of the time – well, okay, be honest: for a while there, it was *most* of the time – I was too obliterated to care. Maybe it was time to start caring.

So I bought curtains and Benjamin and I divided up chores. (No housekeeping – I wasn't going to get that domestic. That's what cleaning services are for.) Robert gave me a cookbook as a housewarming present, at which I initially looked askance and finally, on week three, opened dubiously. Maybe I could try cooking something, I thought. It would surprise Benjamin. It sure as hell would surprise me.

I wasn't working out of my bedroom anymore, which was a big change. There was a den in the new place, and I happily settled in, with my overstuffed sofa and my television and my bookcases filled to overflowing with all the books I'd kept in boxes in my mother's attic on South Battery Street in Charleston for all these years. It was the first time I could ever have them all in one place, and I was giddy with delight.

The telephone numbers hadn't changed. My business was still flourishing, and no one, not my clients or my employees, knew that this momentous change had happened in my life. Which was exactly the way I wanted it to be.

My professional life was certainly not slowing down one iota. In fact, there was always something new and exciting happening, though sometimes I could do with a little less of the excitement.

I sent Tiffany to see Dave Willis out in Sudbury the first weekend we were in the new place. She hadn't even bothered, when I hired her, to give me her real name; or perhaps Tiffany *was* her real name. Maybe there were parents somewhere who looked at their beautiful baby girl and assigned her that ludicrous name. Stranger things have happened.

Dave Willis was a regular; Tiffany was semi-regular, pretty, fresh, popular with the clients despite what I could only consider a total lack of personality. Well, no, I guess she was perky enough, but she was definitely one of the no-small-talk, let's-get-down-to-business girls.

Which I knew would be fine with Dave. He was on the upper end of middle age, with two failed marriages in his past and lingering child support and alimony in his present. I think his only form of recreation was calling the service, that and watching TV, and he pretty much scheduled the girls who came to see him to carefully allow for his TV viewing schedule. Dave was one of those clients who wouldn't see somebody if she was late, so I always sent really reliable girls to his place. I didn't want to lose his business.

Tiffany, to my relief, arrived promptly and checked in with me about thirty seconds after the hour. This, I thought complacently, was going to be one of the good ones. She probably wouldn't need to be called out – Dave usually finished well before the hour was up and sent the girl on her way – but I noted the time anyway, and went on with a more complicated call I was trying to set up, getting two girls from wildly different places in Boston coordinated to arrive together at one of the airport hotels – no small feat.

When the telephone rang twenty minutes later, I thought nothing of it.

"Peach?" It was Tiffany, sounding younger and more vulnerable than I had heard her before; I almost didn't recognize the voice.

"What's up?"

There was a sob on the other side of the line and a pause while she apparently got herself together. I could hear the fear in her voice. "Tiffany? What's the problem?"

"Peach – Peach –"

"Calm down, honey," I said, firmly and as soothingly as I could, putting out my cigarette in the ashtray next to me as though girding myself for action. "I can't help you until you tell me what the problem is." But my mind was racing frantically. What problem could there possibly be with Dave Willis?

"Peach ..." Another long, shuddering breath and she was able to say it. "He's dead."

I had to remind myself to breathe. I had to remind myself that this girl was scared and was counting on me to help her. "Tiffany, okay, honey, you're okay. Just take a deep breath, honey. Take a deep breath and tell me what happened."

She took two long, shaking, shuddering breaths. Another call was coming in and I ignored it. "Peach, it wasn't my fault ..."

"Of course it wasn't, honey. But you have to tell me what happened so I can help you." What did she mean, it wasn't her fault? Had she *killed* him?

"I think it was a heart attack, Peach. It happened so fast. I mean, like, really fast. Like, I was on top of him with his – his thing inside me – and he just kind of gasped, and I thought that meant he was liking it, so I, like, started going faster, only I wasn't really looking at his face, you know?" A brief pause. "Then he wasn't moving or saying anything, and I looked at him and he's this really weird purple color, Peach, so I got off him – I mean, how gross, a dead man's dick inside me, only he was still hard, and I checked and he's not breathing at all."

"Okay." I'd had time to think. It wasn't the first time that sex had induced a fatal heart attack, and at least now I knew what I was dealing with. "Tiffany, you need to hang up and call 911."

"What?" Her voice had risen at least an octave. "I can't do that!"

"You have to do that," I said, firmly. "They're not going to arrest you. But they have to take care of Dave."

"No!" There was a little wild scrabbling on the other end of the line. "Oh, God, my fingerprints are everywhere!"

This was a novel reaction. "Why does that matter? Have you been arrested before?" She had said no, when I had hired her.

"Just once. In New York." Her voice had a slightly sullen tone to it now. "And it was a long time ago."

A long time ago for someone Tiffany's age could be measured in months rather than years, but I was starting to lose patience with her. "Honey, listen. Get dressed. Call 911. They'll come, they'll see what happened, they'll take your name and telephone number and that's all there is to it." Or so I rather fervently hoped.

Okay, I'll be honest: yes, there was a part of me that agreed with Tiffany's obvious desire to just bolt. Pretend it hadn't happened. Get on with things. No one wants to talk to the police, especially when what you're doing is clearly illegal. Vice wasn't going to ride along on an ambulance call, but it still left a queasy feeling in one's stomach, and I won't deny that I was wondering if Dave had left my number next to his telephone.

But it was the thought of Dave – alone, without a wife, without a lot of friends, with children who lived three states away – that kept me on the line with Tiffany. He was an honest man. I wasn't going to leave his body to rot alone in his suburban house until somebody noticed the smell. I'd like to think I was more decent than that.

So I called them myself.

I called from my private number and I used my real name and said that a friend had called me. I gave his address and told them what had happened and that was that. Oddly, I never heard back from either the police or Tiffany. I did later see a notice of Dave's funeral arrangements in the newspaper. I wondered which ex-wife had made them.

I was more than ever grateful for Benjamin. If I died, he would be there. He would care, and I wouldn't be alone in a suburban home with a television remote near my hand and a nameless girl giving me sex for money.

What I wasn't even remotely prepared for, however, was the next installment in the Abby-Benjamin saga.

BABY MAKES THREE

I was pregnant.

The thing you least expect is what happens to you. I've always been convinced of that, and my own life has absolutely proven it to me.

Like most of my friends, I have invested a great deal of effort and money and anxiety into making sure that I don't end up *enceinte*. If you're careful, it doesn't happen, not in this day and age. On the other hand, I had had lapses in the past and nothing had come of them – apparently I didn't conceive easily – so I think that my lackadaisical attitude toward birth control did have some foundation in reality. I wasn't on the pill when it happened, and up until then, nothing had happened, or so I assumed.

Oops.

Benjamin was just finishing his last semester at the North Bennett Street School; he was already working part-time for a restoration company on the North Shore and had in fact been up on Gloucester's Eastern Point for most of that week, doing some work on one of the crumbling mansions up there. I had absolutely no idea how he was going to react.

That I was thinking about his reaction at all was indicative of a major sea change in my outlook on life. In the past, had the question arisen, I couldn't imagine consulting the other individual involved: my body, my decision, and not a difficult one to make. But life with Benjamin was different somehow. I couldn't imagine not telling him, and I couldn't imagine what his reaction might be.

It's always been my philosophy to do everything with a flourish, so I called him on his cell phone. "Hey. Any good restaurants up in Gloucester?"

He sounded bemused. "Depends on your definition of good," he said, cautiously. "Good fish places."

I wrinkled my nose, but forged on nevertheless. "Thought I'd take the train up and meet you for dinner."

"What about work?" He meant mine, of course.

"I can get Evelyn to do the phones." Evelyn – or Taylor, as the clients called her – was as happy doing the phones as she was going on calls. She had just the right touch with clients, too. On a slow night, she could fit in a call herself between the phones, so she ended up happy either way.

"Sure," Benjamin said. "Come into West Gloucester, and call me from the station. I'll pick you up there. Gotta get back to work, hon."

"Okay, I'll see you later." I disconnected. This was going to be fine, I told myself. Whatever happened would be fine. Or so I fervently hoped.

* * * * * *

The Gull restaurant is tucked away inside the Cape Ann Marina, almost invisible unless you know what you're looking for. Once you're there, however, it's pretty unforgettable: floor-to-ceiling windows face the pleasure boats moored on the Annisquam River, all of them ready to head out to sea for a day of fishing, whale watching, or just relaxing.

I had been watching them coming and going for almost an hour, and hadn't yet found a way of saying what I was there to say.

Benjamin wasn't aware of my discomfort. He had picked me up at the train platform – the stops on the commuter rail running out of Boston hardly qualify as stations – and driven me by the castle-like edifice that he and a team from the North Bennett Street School were currently working on, proudly showing me his handiwork before bringing me here. "They have prime rib, too," he said with enthusiasm, handing me a menu. "George comes here almost every day for lunch."

I had no idea who George was. I cared even less. I ordered wine and then after two sips remembered that I wasn't supposed to be drinking, if I was really pregnant, if we were going to keep the baby, if, if, if. The nausea that had prompted me, almost incidentally, to buy the pregnancy test was back.

I pushed some salad around on a plate for a while and then I did the same with some seafood au gratin, trying not to look at Benjamin's prime rib (which he ordered rare, naturally), and finally decided that I didn't know how to say it. "I have to tell you something," I said, only at that moment realizing that he had been in the middle of explaining something to me about cornices. "I'm sorry. I don't mean to be rude. I didn't mean to interrupt."

Concern creased his forehead. "What's up?"

I thought about all the ways I had practiced saying this on the train ride and then gave up. Wordlessly, I opened my purse, took out the plastic pregnancy tester, and passed it across the table to him.

And then I threw up.

* * * * * *

There are moments in my life when I imagine myself to be one of the elegant divas of days gone by: Audrey Hepburn, Katharine Hepburn, Grace Kelly, Lauren Bacall.

But in my heart of hearts, in those moments when reality takes over, I realize that I am and will be forever closest to Lucille Ball as Lucy Ricardo.

Certainly throwing up in a restaurant is more up her alley than anybody else's.

Everyone was very sweet, I'll say that for them. The mess was cleaned up quickly and efficiently; Benjamin stayed behind to deal with the bill and apologies, while I sat and waited outside on the dock. It creaked from time to time, which suited me well; I was feeling fairly creaky myself.

A footstep, and Benjamin sat down beside me. "Well, that's all set."

"I'm sorry," I said, miserably, inadequately. "That was awful."

He put his arm around my shoulders. "I'll say this, it was memorable. We'll be able to tell our first-born that he or she was making waves from the very beginning."

I half-turned to face him. "You mean ..." My voice trailed off. I was suddenly too tired to articulate anything.

Benjamin pulled the long slender plastic tester out of his pocket. "Here we go," he said, taking out a pen, clicking it open. Frowning slightly with concentration, he inscribed the date, then handed it to me. "A souvenir," he said, with a smile. "A souvenir of the beginning."

And that was how we found out about Sam. It was, suddenly, just that simple.

TAKING CHARGE

Benjamin and I may have decided that we were okay with the idea of having a child, but that didn't mean that I'd even begun to assimilate exactly what it meant for my life. I wasn't ready to be pregnant, to buy the books, to think about the clothes ... oh, God, to not see my feet for nearly a year. Ugh. I was still a madam, after all. Sleek and sexy, someone to whom accidents don't happen. It was hard to make those two perceptions – those two *realities* – combine in a way that made sense for me.

My immediate response was to ignore the pregnancy. I saw a doctor and took some extra vitamins and made some half-hearted attempts to quit smoking; I had wine only once a week and eliminated drugs altogether; and that was it.

It wasn't as though my life didn't hold enough challenges. Three days after the dinner in Gloucester

I turned on the local news and heard that a prostitute, a woman who worked the streets down on Kneeland Street, had been murdered. Nice of them to note, I thought sourly, that she had been a prostitute. Much better news value than had she been a waitress, an investment banker, or an administrative assistant. Of course, if she had been any of those things, she also would probably still have been alive. Denying the danger inherent in any line of work that's illegal and attracts people with problems is denying the obvious.

While I offer my employees more security and less exposure to ongoing violence than they'd have if they worked the streets, with or without a pimp, there's still that specter in the background for me.

I read recently that some city in Canada – Montreal, perhaps – has started a database of DNA samples from local prostitutes; if something happens to them, their bodies can be identified more easily. Quite a few of them have signed – a sad and scary commentary on a prostitute's life. It presumes not only that a violent end is a real possibility, but that there will be no one around who knows them and can identify their remains. I shiver when I think about it, and I try very hard not to think about it.

The one inevitable result of my moving into a new space with Benjamin and of becoming pregnant was that I had a tremendous nesting urge. I was loving Charlestown even more than I had Bay Village. It was quirky, a little upscale, and a little strange, the kind of place where I immediately and wonderfully felt at home.

Benjamin and I walked all over Charlestown that first spring. We even made the requisite tourist visit to the Constitution, but mostly we strolled, through squares filled with fragrant lilac and spreading wisteria, up narrow cobbled streets lit by old-fashioned gas lamps. My major coup was being able to secure a table at Olive's on a fairly regular basis; that alone is worth its weight in gold.

I finally started telling a few people – really, really good friends – that I was, as the euphemism goes, expecting. I tried a whole lot of different ones – euphemisms, that is. Preggers. Knocked up. Benjamin suggested the old "bun in the oven" and I threw a pillow at him. To say that people were surprised was the understatement of the century.

I guess that was really my fault, though. For years I had tried to surround myself with a mystique, an air of sophistication, this sense of me being more Peach than Abby, and perceptions don't change just because your heart does.

I didn't let any of the clients know, of course. They were quite sure that they knew what I looked like. High-heeled shoes, seamed stockings, a little black-nothing dress, long legs up on the desk as I leaned back and talked to them – that was the illusion. Even at the time when I bought into my own mystique, I never dressed like that for work; comfort was always the first priority. But I was a magician with words, with inflection, with the tone of my voice. I'd imply just about anything, I'd *lie* about just about anything. The sexier the clients think I am, the better my business.

To this day, my clients know nothing about my private life, my marriage, my son, where I live, what I do, what I look like. Peach is still a figment of their imaginations, and of mine.

* * * * * *

Jill started working for me shortly after I moved to Charlestown with Benjamin.

I was delighted. For one thing, she was absolutely, sensationally gorgeous – skin like ivory, a pre-Raphaelite face framed by wavy black hair, dark eyes. She had just gotten out of the Israeli army and wanted to make as much money in as short a time as she could. Which was perfectly fine with me.

She had no car, but what she did have was limitless energy and a willingness to go on any call, anywhere, at any time, which I appreciated more than I could articulate. At times it feels as though I employ nothing but prima donnas: I can't see that one, I can't do calls before seven, after nine, on Thursdays, in the suburbs, in Southie, with an Asian, with a married man – the list was long and so comprehensive that sometimes I felt like I needed a database to keep up with it all. A *big* one.

But Jill was fine doing whatever – or whomever – and whenever, and the clients loved her. She was young, fresh, and good at doing sales in addition to her other responsibilities, something I didn't see all that frequently.

Once I made an appointment for her to see a client out in the suburbs. I arranged for a car taking another one of the girls who was calling on another client in the same town to drop her off first. The other girl finished her call and came back to pick up Jill, only to find that the client wanted to extend his time another hour. "Only if you'll see both of us," she told him, pouting prettily; and so he agreed, and ended up with the two of them for an additional two hours.

Now, I'm not saying that I couldn't have arranged the same deal, but Jill did a lot of my work for me.

When she saw a client she liked, she never hesitated to pressure him into booking her again, right away, on the spot. "I'm free tomorrow night, shall we say eight o'clock?" she'd say as she was getting dressed, and before he knew what had happened I'd be calling him to confirm the appointment. Maybe it was the Israeli army thing, I don't know, but I can't remember any guy saying no to Jill, not even once.

Hell, they said no to me, all the time.

I'd book her on busy nights for three calls in a row and she'd still be wanting more. I wondered what she did about freshening up between those calls, since I had drivers taking her directly from one to the next, but no one was complaining. The truth is that she was making me a lot of money and I wasn't about to look too closely at how she did it. I was pretty sure that she wasn't cheating or stealing clients from me. For one thing, she didn't have the time; I was keeping her so busy. For another thing, I always know when one of the girls tries to steal a regular. He may be infatuated with someone in the short term, but in the long term his real relationship is with me, and he knows it. I'm part mother confessor, part dominatrix. They always come back, begging for forgiveness, sounding like cheating husbands as they plead the weakness of the moment and promise to never, ever, ever do it again.

And just like any other cheating husband, they will. So I make them pay for it for a while by having them see girls no one wants to see, and then I forgive them, and the whole cycle starts up again, repetitive and predictable. So much for the glamour of it all!

I didn't think that Jill was stealing clients – at least, not regularly enough to counterbalance the prodigious amount of money she was bringing in. I also knew it wasn't going to last very long. No one sees clients at that rate for any sustained period of time: they all burn out. The ones who last are the ones who pace themselves. Margot only went on calls on weekends; Jen, after a few months in the business, only went on one call on any given evening; Cam only saw clients if she had already had a good workout that day. And they lasted. With people like Jill, I always think that three months is the cut-off point. You can do anything for three months. Beyond that lies burnout, and I watch for that, because it's when you're burned out that you make mistakes. Oh, maybe not the kinds of mistakes that make you want to register your DNA with the local police, but mistakes all the same. And I don't want them happening on my watch.

A month went by, and Benjamin and I bought a new dining room set. It was hard for me to imagine when something like that would rock my world, since takeout on the coffee table had always been my norm until then. I didn't even have a dining room in my old apartment in Bay Village. Now here we were with this gorgeous wrought-iron and glass table, these tapestry chairs, and they were there in large part thanks to the income I was getting from Jill.

The first hint of trouble came, as it always does, from the clients themselves. John Richter called me one evening and asked for a call, and I said that Jill was available.

"Um, Peach, that's okay. Is there anybody else?"

"Why, John, what's wrong?" Because I knew there was something. John was sweet and easygoing, and I don't think that he had ever before in the four or five years I'd known him rejected anybody I'd sent to him.

He cleared his throat. Twice. That had to be a bad sign. "It's just that – oh, Peach, it's okay. It's probably just me. You can send Jill."

"No, John, if there's a problem, I need to know about it. Please tell me."

Another throat clearing. "Well, it's not like it's anything bad, you know. I think that maybe I'm wrong, maybe it's my imagination or something …"

Just get *on* with it, I thought impatiently. "I'm sure it's not," I soothed. "Listen, this is my business. It's important to me that you're happy. You'd be doing me a huge favor if you'd help me here."

A deep breath. "Well, you know, she never actually asks for a tip –"

She'd *better* not, I thought savagely.

"– but she makes you feel bad if you don't give her something extra, you know?"

"I have absolutely no idea what you're talking about," I said.

John was floundering. He was a lawyer, I remembered irrelevantly. I devoutly hoped he wasn't this much at sea when he was in front of a jury. "Um … well … she *hints*," he managed to blurt out.

"She never says anything outright, but she makes you feel like you have to do what she's hinting at."

"Like what?" I didn't know if I was fascinated or repulsed.

"Like, you know, I said I was going to get tickets to the Boston Pops, and she made me feel like I should get her some at the same time. So I did." He sounded shamefaced, as well he should. Jill was showing an unanticipated turn of enterprise here. "Go on," I said grimly. There had to be more.

"Well, that's it, really. I mean, there's other stuff ..."

"What kind of stuff?" He was making me pull teeth, and I was suddenly angry with Jill, for making this nice ordinary man feel so bad.

"Well, I mentioned that I was buying some new dishes, so she let me know ... she made me feel that I should give her my old ones."

"John, I'm sorry," I said helplessly.

He was on a roll. "Then there was my Gretzky jersey," he said, plaintively. "My brother-in-law had it signed for me ..."

"John, I'm appalled –"

"... and some of my mother's jewelry. She wanted to try it on while we were – um – having sex, you know, and I told her she looked so good in it – and she did, Peach, really, it was all flashy and brilliant on her, and I said she could borrow it, and she said no, she'd be too afraid she'd become too attached to it to return it, so of course I said …"

Of course you did.

"And then she had this friend who didn't work for you, who didn't want to work for a service, but Jill had told her about me and she really wanted to do a double with Jill, so I said yes."

Yikes, it was getting me where I lived now. "John," I said, firmly, to stem the torrent, "John, thank you for telling me. Jill won't come by to see you tonight. In fact, Jill won't be seeing anyone anymore."

"You can't do that!" he yelped.

"Why on earth not?" I'd have thought it was exactly what he wanted.

"She'll know it was me," he spluttered. "She'll know I told you, Peach, and she knows my phone number, she knows where I live, she knows where I work –"

Why did she know where he worked?

"I took her there once, you know, when I had her over for a couple of hours. We did it on the desk." He sounded embarrassed, and I pictured the high ceilings and sweeping views of the building on the waterfront where I knew he worked. "And maybe even introduced her to my partner once, I can't remember …"

He was backpedaling. Not only had he introduced her, she was now seeing the partner – I would have bet my last dollar on it. That wasn't stealing a client, technically, if I was correctly understanding Jill's way of thinking.

"And I know she'll be mad, I just know that she will …"

Whoa, Nellie. This successful fifty-something attorney, partner in an important Boston practice, doesn't want to make a twenty-one-year-old pre-college student *mad* at him? "John, I won't tell her that you spoke to me at all."

"She'll know!" There was a rising note of hysteria in his voice. "She'll know it was me, Peach, I swear she will!"

"Don't be silly," I said briskly, in my best no-nonsense nanny voice. "John, listen to me. Listen to me. You have to get a grip. I'll talk to some other people, okay? You know that if this was happening with you, it was happening with other people, too." If he had been in front of me, I would have slapped him across the face to wake him up. "John? John, are you listening?"

"Yes, Peach," he murmured meekly.

"I will not tell Jill that you and I spoke. I'll talk to some other people and then I'll talk to her and I swear that she will not come after you. But you know that you should have told me this a very long time ago."

"I know, Peach."

"Okay. It's all going to be all right." I took a deep breath. "In the meantime, I'm going to send Sarah over to see you tonight, as a special treat. She's gorgeous, blonde, slim, and she's thinking about going into law. I know that you'll have a good time."

"Okay, Peach. Thank you."

"It's my pleasure, John." I hung up the phone and thought, *I'm going to kill that girl.*

A ROMANTIC AT HEART

Jill was going to resurface. They always do, especially the ones about whom you have mixed feelings.

In the meantime, life goes on. I hate firing people and do it only when absolutely necessary. In a world where connections are everything, you don't want to sever too many of them. So I let her go into whatever oblivion she had gone into. I'd deal with her later. I wanted to deal with my personal life for a while.

If you asked me to say, off the top of my head, where my favorite place in the world is, I'd have to reply that it's Block Island. If you've not heard of it, that's just fine with me, though someone, somewhere, called it one of the last great places in America.

When I first moved to Boston and was going to Emerson, some cycling enthusiast friend talked me into taking a day trip there. "We'll rent bikes when we arrive. It'll be great," she assured me. I was enchanted by the ferry ride, a lot less enchanted by the cycling. (I'm not averse to exercise, but I'd rather be moving through clear water than up a dusty hill in the hot sun.) I looked at the old Victorian hotels lining the waterfront and felt a tug back in time, to an era of elegance and beauty, where afternoon tea was served, croquet was played, and people still dressed for dinner. I fell in love with Block Island then and have never fallen out of love with it since.

I nearly went there with Jesse once, but he bailed at the last minute and I stayed home alone and got drunk instead. I was angry about it at the time, but in retrospect I'm glad it happened. I cannot imagine thoughts of Jesse tainting this place now.

Benjamin made it a surprise. "Can you get someone to do the phones for a couple of nights?" he asked, casually, while we were doing laundry together. The townhouse in Charlestown had its own washer and dryer in a closet off the main bathroom. I probably would have loved the luxury more if I hadn't been in the lamentable habit of paying my cleaning people to go and do my laundry in the past.

"Probably. Why?"

He shrugged, his head bent over the socks. "Why is it that they never match when they come out?" he asked rhetorically. "I don't know, Abby, no reason. I'd like to get away and I know you could use it, too. You've been working really hard."

I love it when people notice how hard I'm working. There's a certain self-righteousness about working hard that only really works when people talk about how wonderful you are for doing it. I preened myself. "I suppose I have," I acknowledged, modestly. "So what did you have in mind?"

He straightened up and looked at me. "What about Block Island?"

I didn't ask how he knew about my infatuation with Block Island; Benjamin pays attention to everything. "I'd love to," I said. It's one thing to notice that I like the place and another thing altogether to invite me there. I was feeling a little awed. He was my knight in shining armor, after all.

"Great," Benjamin said, happily unaware of his knighthood status. "I'll call up the hotel. When do you want to go?"

"Anytime," I said, automatically, then regrouped. "Well … what if I work Friday night and we go down Saturday, and stay through Monday. Could you manage that?" Probably not, I thought. He did have a profession, too. Sometimes I tend to forget that I live with somebody who is part of the nine-to-five world. He would probably say no and then we'd argue about whose work took precedence.

"Sure," he said.

I swallowed the arguments I'd been preparing and meekly picked up the laundry basket.

If you ever go, stay at the Hotel Manisses. The hotel is named for the island and is one of the Victorian old ladies, a little creaky and stuffy, but with its elegance still intact despite the need for a facelift and a tighter corset. Our room was named, in the unfortunate custom of the hotel, after a famous local shipwreck, the *Palantine*. It had a whirlpool, a nice post-Victorian touch. But the real attraction is the bar – cocktails extraordinaire, a view of the harbor, and a style that never goes out of style.

We had dinner reservations for seven, and at six headed down to the bar. I was thinking about blue drinks – I've always liked fancifully colored cocktails – but Benjamin had apparently made alternate arrangements in advance, and a bottle of Mumm's champagne was waiting for us.

"What's this?" Okay, so I can be a little slow at times.

Benjamin and the bartender exchanged meaningful looks and the bartender popped the cork – discreetly into his hand – before pouring into the two waiting flutes. He was smiling broadly. I had the nagging feeling that I hadn't zipped up my dress, or something equally embarrassing. "What?" I said again.

"This." He opened the box before handing it to me. Okay, so I can be *very* slow. The solitaire glinted brightly against the blue velvet and, absurdly, there were tears in my eyes.

So maybe this particular madam is a romantic at heart after all.

* * * * * *

Maybe being a romantic has something to do with the layers of rationalization that I used to go through on almost a daily basis.

There's something that happens to you when you spend enough time watching people screw up their lives, when you are the conduit through which they earn money that they then spend on stuff that might kill them.

When I first started my agency, I didn't think much about any of it. I was in complete denial about any downside there might be to the business. I was too high myself from the excitement of doing something forbidden, from the money and the success of the operation, and from my sudden and delightful status in Boston's nightlife to think about much else. It was a very self-involved view of the world; but it's a profession that encourages self-centrism, so it's hard to think how I might have been successful if I'd felt any other way.

But as time passed and my priorities changed, doubts began to creep in. Doubts about whether I was as lily-white and innocent as I told myself – with some frequency – that I was. Doubts about whether I could do what I did and still feel good about myself as a human being.

The reality is that I sent girls to places that I'd never want to go, to do things I'd never want to do, and that, given half a chance, I would do it all over again. Like everybody else, I was in it for the money. And the money was good enough to soothe my conscience for a very long time.

There are phases of justification that you go through. There's the knowledge, in some cases the very sure knowledge, that if the girls didn't work for me, they'd be working for someone else, and probably someone who would treat them far worse than I did. I knew enough about the other services in town, not to mention the street pimps, to know that I was the caviar of the escort world. So this worked pretty well for a while.

Then there was the justification that involved my clientele. Ninety percent of my clients, as I've mentioned, are white-bread, vanilla-sex kinds of guys. They're mostly guys that I've been sending women to for years and years. I know them and, as much as is possible in our little world, I trust them – or at least I trust myself to handle them. So if a girl came to work for me after working for one of the other services, I could rationalize that I was a step up for them, a step toward a better life. Once in a while, a girl would leave the job for something better. Once in a while she'd get past the patchy economics that had placed her in that position and move on, and I'd congratulate myself on having played a role in her success. This, I told myself, meant that I was doing something good.

Then, at some point, I just stopped rationalizing altogether.

These days? I don't feel guilty about what I do, though I also don't try and kid myself that I'm Mother Teresa. We all carry this kind of puritanical history with us in this country. This is the only place where it's okay to watch someone being murdered on television, but you can't show part of a nipple: that's pretty screwed up. I enable two consenting adults to spend an hour together; he gets his jollies, she gets her money, and frankly I don't see a whole lot that's wrong with this.

I also don't see a whole lot there to brag about, either. It's a job. It's always been a job. I just used to romanticize it to the point of parody, and somehow lost track of my own compass in doing so.

There's something exciting about doing something illegal. There's a whole concept in our society of the outlaw as being hip, romantic, and cool, and that's how I saw myself: Outlaw Peach, sexy and seductive, clever and compassionate, the Belle of Boston. It got me through some difficult times and it got me past a whole lot of insecurity that I might not have shed otherwise.

As you get older, though, being an outlaw is less cool. I got pregnant. I got married. Being on the wrong side of the law might well have been a necessary part of my work, but I sure as hell wasn't getting off on it anymore.

So I've gone through being in love with my work, seeing it as glamorous and hip, to being slightly embarrassed by it, to being bored by it, to where I am now: it's my job. I run a certain kind of business, and I run it well. And, like every working wife and mother, there's a certain tricky part in trying to keep everything balanced.

Any female corporate executive would tell you the same thing.

* * * * * *

I was more careful with things once we moved to Charlestown. In the past, I hadn't particularly thought about how my neighbors perceived me. I hadn't particularly thought about my neighbors, period. But now we became friendly with the elderly couple living in the other half of the townhouse, and I knew the people at the market on the corner, where I still went every day to buy cigarettes, even though Benjamin, my mother, his mother, and just about everybody else I knew was urging me to quit.

The people who mattered to me – my friends, my family, even my clients – these were people who pretty much accepted who I was, what I did, everything about me. In the past the only persona that I'd ever wanted to project was that of the hip and successful madam-about-town. Now, however, things were changing, and the way I behaved had to change as well.

I kept the cell phone, but only used it when I was away from the office; land lines are always more secure. I told my catering story until I was blue in the face. I wanted to be someone other than just Peach; I wanted the Abby side of me to be presentable as well.

I don't know if I did that for Benjamin or he did it for me, but by the time we got married I was seeing myself through a different prism. Perhaps, for the first time in my life, I was seeing myself as a whole person: as a Southern woman poet, as a madam, as a wife, as a mother-to-be. I was seeing myself as being made up of all the complicated parts that make us human.

I joined a health club and started swimming every day, sitting by the pool just as I used to sit in cafés, with my leather-bound book open in front of me and the words to the poems I was creating dancing in the air all around me. I wrote about life beginning and life ending, about people who sold their bodies and people who sold their souls. I looked at the impossible chlorine color of the water and imagined lazy sun-drenched islands in the South Seas, impossibly long days, sand between my toes. And I wrote about it all.

Then Sam was born and my world changed forever.

YOU'RE FIRED!

I hadn't fired Jill, despite what I told John Wills. She was going to burn out on her own. In the meantime, I simply wasn't willing to give up the kind of money she brought in. What I did do – I'm not altogether heartless – was change who I was sending her to. Clients like John, who were easily manipulated, couldn't handle someone like Jill, but I had more than enough clients in my repertoire who could match her little act and do her one better. If Jill wanted to play hard, I could play harder.

She was definitely coming unraveled, something I had seen before in others but hadn't anticipated happening to her; she seemed too hard, too tough. I guess it can happen to anybody, but it was unpleasant to watch, uncomfortable, and sometimes nerve-wracking.

Girls are rude to clients all the time; for that matter, clients are rude to girls too. But when girls start being rude to me, there's a line I start drawing. No matter how much I need them, they need me more. There may well be other agencies in town, but there is also a never-ending supply of gorgeous young women in a city like Boston, as endless as the incoming freshman classes that arrive every August in a city that's expensive to live in.

To be perfectly fair to me, I took a lot from Jill before I started drawing that line.

"Hey, Jill, it's Peach. Work."

"Who is it?" A clear yawn on the other end of the line.

"Henry Ramirez. He's in Back Bay. He's a regular. I need you there by eight."

"Do you have anyone else besides him? I don't want to get dressed if I'm only seeing one guy."

"Nothing," I said firmly, amazed at her level of self-absorption. Not to mention rudeness. "I'm not sending you on any more calls. I can't afford to."

There was a sharp intake of breath. "I can't believe you're firing me! After all the business I've brought you!"

I thought of the complaints, the hang-ups, the headaches. "Not worth it, Jill, sorry. You'll have to try another agency."

"I *will*!" The receiver came crashing down, hard. Jill wasn't used to people saying no to her. I was pleased to have had the opportunity to give her the new experience.

What was worse than her attitude was that Jill had managed to alienate my best driver, Cynthia. The reality is that good drivers are worth their weight in gold, and not the easiest people to get along with, either. The irregularity of what they do means that there has to be something unusual about a person who works well as a driver with me. I hesitate to use the word weird, but it's there all the same, right on the tip of my tongue.

First off, you're spending your time driving beautiful women around, but beautiful woman are also self-absorbed. Many of them do drugs. Many of them think nothing of asking you to go out of your way to run errands or do favors for them. And yes, there is the occasional girl willing to augment her fare by giving the drivers an occasional blow job; but, by and large, that's not enough to justify the trouble she puts you through.

Then there is the income. People from the real world, I've found, have some expectations of an ongoing, reasonably steady income, even from part-time jobs, and that simply isn't the case here. One night a driver can make $30, the next night, $150. The amount is generally distance-dependent, and I try to make the client pay at least part of the freight so that it doesn't all cut into the girl's income; I'm moderately successful, I think, in striking a balance there; but it is, at best, erratic.

The hours are horrific, and there is often pressure to get somewhere quickly. There are long periods with nothing to do, or an occasional client who tries to play mind games with the girls by giving them bad directions. Many of the clients live in quiet suburban areas where neighbors would call the police if they saw a strange car parked, waiting, so the driver often has to be creative about how and where to spend that hour while the girl is doing the call.

And, finally, there is the surreal feeling that one gets when one drops a girl off, knowing she's about to have sex with someone, and picks her up after she has done so. I mean, what kind of light conversation fills that particular void? I'm quite sure that's one that Emily Post doesn't cover in her big white book.

At least there *are* drivers. I have my share of single mothers, girls who go on calls with their kids in the back seat, girls who interrupt calls because the babysitter has beeped them with an emergency.

I guess that I started feeling differently about the mothers once I became one myself.

CAN'T GET ENOUGH
OF MUFFY

I never thought that there were actually women who called themselves Muffy.

Don't get me wrong. I grew up in one of the most snobbish and élitest homes one can imagine. We had a whole lot of ways of saying and showing that we were better than anybody else around. We only associated with the "right" people and we were as racist and sexist as any of our forebears; we just showed it differently. There is nothing progressive, much less kind, about high society in Charleston, South Carolina.

Yet I had managed to get through my own expensive Southern prep school and debutante upbringing without ever meeting anybody named Muffy.

Then again, we weren't as big on college educations in the South. We didn't expect internships at *Cosmopolitan* and *Seventeen* to show we have the makings of a career before making the marriage that will cement our future. We went pretty much right for the marriage itself.

Muffy had done the requisite college sorority rituals at Wellesley and then had decided – against everyone's recommendations – to stay on in Boston and work. She wanted to go into banking, a profession that was much respected on the *male* side of her family; and she wanted to do it on her own, which was pretty much unheard of in the circles from which she came.

The only problem was that entry-level positions in the banking industry don't pay the bills. Well, not Muffy's kind of bills, anyway. What with the horse she kept stabled in Hamilton and the shoes from Aldo's on Newbury Street, the requisite Donna Karan and Anna Molinari suits and dresses and the equally requisite appearances at charity balls and dinners – not to mention the condo on Beacon Hill – Muffy was going to have to ask Daddy for help. She'd been asking Daddy for help all her life and was tired of it. So she called me instead.

She showed me a picture of her family once, all of them looking like a royal family – casual, smiling into the late-afternoon Connecticut sun as it streamed down over an expanse of emerald lawn that had to have been trimmed with nail clippers, it was so perfect. Muffy's mother showed what Muffy herself would look like in another twenty years or so, give or take a facelift or two: determined, cheerful, not a hair out of place. She probably organized a lot of charity events to help the poor, who she knew about in the abstract. Muffy's father was smiling broadly, showing off his possessions, a bit of heaviness around the waist and jowls lending an air of seriousness to his demeanor. Her brother, Harrison (following the perfectly absurd WASP tradition of giving sons first names that are interchangeable with surnames), attended country day school in the picture but was on his way to Princeton and a seat on his father's board of directors. Muffy and her sister Kerry were loose-limbed, tanned, entitled. It was the perfect family; it was everything that everybody else in the country wanted to be.

The clients couldn't get enough of Muffy. She was everything that they wanted, too: the elusive high school girl that none of them had ever managed to date because she lived in a different world, a different galaxy. Muffy was the girl they had never dared ask to the prom, because she wouldn't have even known that they existed. Even then, in the 1990s, in the middle of the dot-com boom, when being a nerd was a good thing, all my little entrepreneurial clients could remember, when they met Muffy, was how they had been in the chess club when she was the homecoming queen. Muffy made them realize just how nouveau *nouveau riche* actually was.

But there was a light at the end of their tunnel. Thanks to the wonderful world of capitalism, they too could have a Muffy of their very own. At least for an hour at a time.

She wore little black-nothing dresses and pearls and perfume to go on calls, flashed seamed stockings that cost $50 a pair, and got outrageous tips. She was laughingly insulting, too sure of herself to feel any qualms about sharing her true reactions. I think that for some of the guys, being insulted by Muffy was better than being complimented by any of the other girls.

Like most of the women who work for me, Muffy knew nothing about my private life. To her I was Peach, with an office somewhere that she really didn't care much about. She drove herself to her calls in an antique Jaguar E-type that had been her siblings' graduation gift (her parents had given her a down payment on her condo to celebrate the same occasion) and met one of my drivers every so often to pay the fees she was holding for me.

One day, though, I really needed to get some cash from her, and Andy, my current driver-errands guy, was nowhere to be found. I called Muffy and arranged to meet her at Sonsie's on Newbury Street. I was late; I usually am. I think that I plan things perfectly but the world always seems to intervene between me and my schedule. But it didn't matter, because she was later. I had ordered a latte and pastry when she showed up, and I have to say that, jaded as I am both to inherited wealth and to beautiful women, Muffy still managed to take my breath away. She was actually wearing a cashmere twin set and a plaid skirt and a string of pearls. I had thought that people put those on for portraits. Her honey-colored hair was perfect. Her creamy skin was flawless. I suddenly thought of all the hyphenated Americans I had on my client roster and how, for them, having sex with Muffy must be like sleeping with the Mayflower itself.

She didn't apologize, just took her seat and turned a six-hundred-watt smile on the waiter, who immediately succumbed and rushed her a dry martini with a lot more alacrity than he had brought my coffee. "Peach! It's you! I'm so *thrilled* to meet you!"

I smiled amiably and handed her the book I'd been reading. She blinked at it. "If you can put the money in the book," I suggested delicately, and she laughed, really laughed, tipping her head back, enjoying herself. I'd never seen a woman laugh like that. I was fascinated.

She took an envelope from her Gucci bag and slid it into the book, which she then passed back to me. "I feel so James Bond," she said, the laughter still in her eyes and her voice and playing with the edges of her mouth. "What fun, Peach! It's much more boring when I give it to Andy!"

I stirred my latte. "I like to be discreet." Almost immediately, my telephone rang. Okay, so much for being discreet. I feel comfortable with myself, and yet I swear this woman made me feel like I had two left hands. "Excuse me a moment."

It was Siobhan, Sam's nanny. "I'm sorry to bother you, Mrs. Townsend," she said, her Irish accent sharp and melodic across the phone line. "But Sam's little friend Jamie wants him to come play at his house. D'you mind if I take him on over? I'll have him back before supper."

"That's fine." Sam was a precocious two-and-a-half, and already at ease with other kids. I almost wished that he were more dependent on me. "Just leave the number in the kitchen for me, won't you?"

"Sure thing, Mrs. Townsend."

I pressed the off button. Muffy was watching me. "My son," I explained, helplessly. Not only did I rarely meet the women who work for me, I certainly never let them know I have a family.

"You have a son?" Had she been brought up anywhere but in private schools in Connecticut, her voice would have been a squeal. "Oh, Peach, you have to show me a picture!"

The waiter brought her martini, and she flashed him The Smile again. I almost told her not to bother, that he was clearly gay, but then I realized that she wasn't turning it on for him in particular, that it was something she had learned a long time ago, probably the day the braces came off and revealed those perfect white teeth. I was going to have to start charging clients extra for that smile, I thought.

I guess there's a first time for everything. I pulled out my wallet and opened it to the picture portfolio, carefully sliding Sam's pictures out from the rest. Benjamin was there, too, but I wasn't going to invite comment on my husband. There's just so close I'm going to let anyone come.

Muffy took the pictures from me and looked at them slowly, seriously, really looking at them. "He's gorgeous," she breathed. She kept studying his face and it was starting to give me the creeps. I reached across to take the pictures from her.

She looked up and met my eyes. There was a slight flush on her cheeks and her eyes were bright. "He's beautiful," she said, again, and handed the pictures back. "You're so amazing, Peach. You run a business and you have a family."

I wasn't feeling particularly amazing. "It's a matter of priorities," I said, as though I had set out and planned the life I had. I'd very nearly lost Benjamin by not taking him seriously enough; and Sam, who was truly the most delightful part of my life, had been conceived completely by accident. But no one needed to know that.

"I know ..." Muffy's voice had gotten dreamy. She sipped her martini and watched people walking by outside. Newbury Street is one of those places where you can sit in a café and watch people and eventually see the same ones go by, once, twice, three times, as much there to be seen as to see. "Back in college," she said, making it sound like she was referring to something that had happened decades before, "I was so much in love … he was perfect, Peach, warm and kind and sexy." She shivered. She was speaking to me, but watching the people walking by in the sunshine. "I thought of him as mine, somehow. I thought that everything – I don't know – whenever I looked into the future, he was there, he was part of it. Any future I could imagine, I could only imagine with him in it."

"What happened?"

She shrugged. "I lost him," she said. "I lost him, and I thought there couldn't be any more futures. That was when I decided to stay on here and get a job. I decided to build something that wasn't dependent on someone else being part of it."

I didn't know what to say. "I'm sorry."

The impossible green eyes looked at me directly for the first time. "I'm not," Muffy said, her voice a little surprised. "Too many women are afraid of losing someone, so they don't try." She sipped her drink again, delicately, as though savoring its taste. "I thought that nothing counted anymore, because I'd lost him. All I could think about was the loss, not the fact that I once had had him and was happy then. And that's what matters, in the end. We're made up of what we've had, not what we've lost."

Interesting to see it all in terms of ownership, I thought. But now Muffy was moving along, brisk and superficial again, pulling out her own snapshot, the picture of her family smiling into the late afternoon Connecticut sun with the palatial white mansion behind them, the future in their genes, and I understood her perspective. She seemed to have sifted a little wisdom through that prism of WASP entitlement, after all.

She was on and off my radar for the rest of that year, though I didn't give her a lot of thought, any more than I gave any of my employees a lot of thought. As I said, it didn't do to think too much about them as individuals; it got in the way of business. I sent Muffy on calls and the clients continued to adore her, and the afternoon we'd spent together at Sonsie's faded away. Sometimes I wondered if I had dreamed it all.

Sam's fifth Christmas, the skirt that had seemed too tight after coming back from the cleaners told the tale: I was pregnant again. Benjamin had long since graduated from the North Bennett Street School, and was working on a home restoration over on Brattle Street in Cambridge. He was scared out of his head about an expanding family, and yet at the same time so excited that he tended to babble about it to anyone who would listen. For someone who had never thought he'd have children, Benjamin had taken to fatherhood with delight.

The rent had been raised on our townhouse in Charlestown yet again, and he was getting itchy about that. Somehow, in his mind, being settled and owning one's own house go hand in hand, and he felt that we had waited long enough as it was. I wasn't going to be able to get a mortgage in my name, obviously, though I could certainly provide the down payment. He'd been working long enough for what was becoming a terrific salary that we were going to do just fine.

A woman who used to work for me, Caro, in deciding to "go legit," had gone into real estate. By now she was a partner in a real estate company over on Beacon Street, and well-connected with mortgage lenders. Caro, we decided, would be able to make the forms work for us instead of against us.

If I was paying less attention to work than usual, there were some very good reasons: I was pregnant, and we were spending all of our spare time looking at houses, talking about where we'd like to live, and exploring potential communities around Boston. Or maybe I'm just making excuses for not noticing that Muffy hadn't been calling.

Girls drop in and out of the life. They get boyfriends and stop working, then the relationship ends and they come back. They get a job and stop working, then come back from time to time when they need extra money. My concern is with the here and now: who can work tonight, who can work this weekend. I'm not supposed to be holding anybody's hand. Or so I need to keep reminding myself.

I got the call one dreary January day, when the afternoon shadows were lengthening toward twilight and the wind was making the windows rattle. The room was dark and I was feeling sick from the pregnancy and hadn't gotten up to put on any lights. Benjamin would be home soon, and Siobhan would be leaving. When he got here he'd set all the rooms ablaze with light and we'd have an early dinner and some family time before I had to turn the phones on. That was all I was thinking about when the call came.

It was a young man's voice, a cultured voice. "Hello, may I please speak with Peach?"

It was the phone line I give the girls to use. I frowned and pulled the shawl I was wearing tighter around me. Perhaps I already had a premonition, I don't know. All that I remember feeling is suddenly, uncomfortably cold. "This is Peach."

"Ah, yes. Hello. This probably is sounding a little strange to you …" There was the slightest of pauses, and then he resumed, his voice a little louder, a little more assured. I had a mental picture of someone trying to get a grip on himself. "My name is Harrison

Granville. I believe that you may know my sister, Melissa Granville, in some context?"

That voice, that name ... I thought of the summer afternoon captured in the photo that Muffy had shown me at Sonsie's, of the emerald green lawn, the deep shadows, and the white mansion in the background. "Muffy?" I asked.

"Yes, we called her Muffy."

Called? "What happened?" I asked, but I think I knew already, feeling my throat constrict, feeling that I was going to throw up.

He cleared his throat. Yes, he was young enough to have been the Abercrombie and Fitch model standing next to her in the picture. "We found your name and number in her address book," he said, carefully. "I'm sorry to tell you that Muffy ... she died three days ago."

"What happened?" I repeated, belatedly adding, "I'm so sorry for your loss."

"Thank you." It was the proverbial stiff upper lip speaking, I was sure of that. "May I ask in what context you knew my sister?"

I swallowed hard, twice, trying to keep the nausea at bay. "We were friends," I whispered, wishing that it were true. "What happened, Harrison?"

There was another pause. He wasn't good at this yet. By the time the funeral was held in the proper Episcopal church in whatever wealthy Connecticut community they lived in, I imagined that he'd be better at it. "My sister took an overdose of sleeping pills," Harrison said finally, carefully. "We are not going to release that information to the media, so I must ask for your discretion."

The room was starting to spin around me, and my stomach lurched. "I'm so sorry –" I blurted. Now I had a hand over my mouth.

"If you would like to be notified about memorial arrangements," he began, diffidently, but I couldn't wait. "No, no thank you," I managed to gasp. "I'm so sorry." By the time I pressed the off button I was halfway to the bathroom. I almost made it.

I dragged myself across the cold tile floor to the toilet, hugging it in the age-old position, feeling the cold against my forehead. I closed my eyes. I was back in Atlantic City, with the pills all neatly in a line, ready to be swallowed. Ready to take me where I thought I wanted to go. My father's voice, echoing through the years: "I want to see my girl." And the closed door, the denials, the stupid shrine that my mother had erected to his memory, the sheer inconsequence of it all. How many times does death seem preferable to life? To sleep, to dream, to drift off someplace where feelings don't have to be felt, decisions don't have to be made, nothing has to be done. To not only not be afraid of the darkness, but to welcome it. God, the temptation is always there, isn't it?

For all my own attempts at suicide, half-hearted and otherwise, I had never known anyone who killed themselves, much less someone who had worked for me.

I sat on the cold tile floor and cried for Muffy.

* * * * * *

Later, lying in bed with a cold washcloth over my forehead and Benjamin gently stroking my arm, I tried to talk about it. "I wonder why."

His voice in the darkness was very close. "Who knows," he said, softly. "Maybe it was all too much for her, the expectations her family had."

"I thought she had a pretty good handle on those expectations," I said. "Oh, God, Benjy, it couldn't be anything that happened on a call, could it?"

"Of course not," he said immediately, stoutly reassuring. "Girls work for you every day, none of them get upset enough to kill themselves."

"That we know of," I said darkly.

He wasn't having any of it. "Abby, you have to let that go. You're not in charge of the world. She hadn't gone on a call in weeks, right?" I nodded numbly. We'd already started dissecting it at dinner, when Benjamin very wisely called Jane to take over the phones for me. I had managed about three bites of lasagna before I was back in the bathroom throwing up. "So it wasn't a reaction to anything that happened here," he said reasonably.

"I'm trying to remember who she saw last." It had been weeks ago, and I don't keep records. Usually I pride myself on not keeping them. "I can't remember. Maybe it was Carl Lianza – that guy at the Four Seasons. She used to see him a lot."

"It doesn't matter," Benjamin said again. "It wasn't about you, Abby."

"No, I know," I said, irritably. "Even I am not so obtuse or self-centered that I can't see that someone's committing suicide may not be about me."

"I didn't mean that," he said, hurt.

"I know." But I was feeling bad and lashing out was a primeval response. It's more than a truism that misery loves company. "But you didn't know her."

"Neither did you," he pointed out. "She worked for you, Abby. You met her, what? Once? And suddenly you're all concerned that you might have contributed to her suicide? It's never that easy."

Somewhere in the back of my mind a voice was cautioning me to go no further, and I remembered, belatedly, that someone in Benjamin's past had killed himself. A cousin, was it? An uncle? A girl was dead, a family grieved, and all I could do was make my husband – who was doing nothing but trying to make me feel better – feel worse. Nice going, Abby.

And then it was as though she were in the room with us, for I could hear her voice that clearly. Words I never thought I'd remember were echoing in my head: "I thought that none of it counted, because I'd lost him, because all I could think about was the loss. Not the fact that I once had had him and was happy then. And that's what matters, in the end. We're made up of what we've had, not what we've lost."

I started to cry. For what she had had, and not for what she had lost.

* * * * * *

After Muffy died, I noticed a change in my behavior, in my way of looking at things. I took people a lot less for granted, and I started being far more careful about keeping up with people.

Jen hadn't worked for me in over five years, and I had let our friendship lapse, so I called her. She seemed surprised to hear from me, and cautiously pleased; it turned out that she was getting married herself. "Didn't think I ever would," she said.

"What made you change your mind?" I asked.

"I met someone I couldn't live without," she said, and I smiled. Sometimes it could just be that simple.

She had a novel coming out soon, she said, the same one she had first thought about in the days she used to read to me in my apartment in Bay

Village. "It was really hard to write," she sighed. "My fiancé – Tony – says the subtitle could be *Jenny Goes to Therapy.* Can you come to a signing?"

"You bet," I assured her, thinking first of all that I already had to do, and then realizing that it was precisely at times like these that you make room for other people in your life. "I'll come to your book signing if you come to my housewarming."

"You've got a deal," she said.

My friend Leo, who used to live near me in Bay Village, was someone else with whom I tried to catch up. We had been close before I moved in with Benjamin, and I had let that relationship lapse, too, without really meaning to. Leo worked as an attorney, but he had a flair for decorating that had always delighted me. "Come look at houses with us!"

He seemed surprised and pleased. "I'm on my way."

Caro found us the perfect house in Watertown, a suburb of Boston that was still close enough to the city that one didn't feel completely isolated but that gave us space to belong, space to move. A library with a terrific children's section; long, leafy paths to walk along the Charles River. People met your eyes and said hello coming out of the shops that lined its two main streets.

The house itself was not wonderful but, as Benjamin said, it had wonderfulness potential. There was a decent-sized yard, sure to win Sam's heart; and it looked as though, for the first time since I had adopted them from the animal shelter, Sid and Court might be able to get outside and try for the occasional bird or squirrel. Neither of them was getting any younger, so I had my doubts about whether it could actually happen, but you know what they say about hope springing eternal in the feline breast. There was a basement in which Benjamin could finally have a venue for practicing with Mnemonic, his on-again, off-again rock band, a tremendously large kitchen (for me to work on my developing culinary skills), a good-sized office, four bedrooms, and a driveway with a detached garage. A driveway! All for us! It seemed too good to be true.

Watertown Public Schools, we were informed, were quite good. There was a health club next door to the supermarket (as well as to the pizza place, but I won't dwell too much on that little irony). And there was a place we could call home.

We bid on the house and fretted ourselves to pieces until Caro finally called with a closing date. The words seemed foreign. I felt as though in some weird way I had come full circle – from outlaw to suburban mom. Benjamin was hugging me.

"No," I said darkly. "I'm warning you right here and now – we are not ever *ever* buying a minivan!"

Never say never.

MOVING ON

Two months after we moved to Watertown, I miscarried.

In the midst of joy, I was plunged back into sorrow. I stayed in, with the blinds drawn. I didn't want to talk to Benjamin; I didn't want to talk to anyone. Business suffered and I came close to closing the agency.

I have no words to describe what I felt. Or what Benjy felt.

It was Sam who brought us out of it. Sam was full of life, full of needs, claiming his own life, and in so doing he brought me back from the brink. I remembered the vase in the hallway, my father, Atlantic City, and I looked at Sam, the devotion in his face, and I finally smiled. I may have gone a little crazy, but at least I knew the way back.

After we lost the baby, I became a philosopher. Actually, it was the juxtaposition of my loss with Mirra that started it all.

Mirra had worked for me five or six years before this all happened, at about the same time that I was pregnant with Sam. She had come out of Montreal's strip clubs and saw Boston as a quick stop on her way out to Los Angeles and the porn industry with its promises of fame and fortune. She did some dancing in Boston, but most of all worked for me while she figured out how to manage LA., which in her case meant finding a man to take care of her as she climbed the rungs of the California ladder to success.

Mirra's plan had worked, too. She soon had a name and was in demand for the most pictures and the sleaziest parties. She stayed in touch with me, for reasons that I didn't quite understand but went along with. Perhaps I was a sort of surrogate mother to her. I had gathered that her mom hadn't exactly been nurturing.

She'd call every couple of months or so, and I chatted with her, updating her on Boston's gossip and listening to her stories about life on the West Coast. She was pretty, though not extraordinarily so. There was a French air about her, though, that the camera caught and magnified, so she seemed like an exotic creature, caught for a moment in an erotic pose before moving off into the shadows to reappear elsewhere, reinvented in yet another exotic persona against the drab milieu of standard-industry porn.

That fall, I got a call from Mirra. She was back in Montreal, and living in a shelter.

"What on earth happened, Mirra?"

There was a silence. "There are lists," she said at last, painfully. "Everything's computerized, you know?"

I had no idea what she was talking about. "What lists, honey?"

I could hear her taking a deep drag on a cigarette and I wished I wasn't trying to quit smoking. "The lists," she said dully, "The ones that say who's infected and who's not."

Oh, God. A cold fist closed and twisted somewhere in my stomach. "Mirra –"

Exhale of smoke. I could almost taste it over the phone line. "And I was careful, Peach. I really was. But they pay you so much more to do it without protection."

I closed my eyes in despair. Sam was trying to get my attention. "You're HIV-positive?"

There was something akin to a sob. "Yes, I just got tested. Then they all said there would be work." She paused. "You know, there was nothing going on for the longest time, I mean, at the beginning. Everyone got it and then they started being safe again ..." Another ragged breath. "They figured out who Patient Zero was this time round. I only had sex with him twice ..."

Dear God. Only twice. "So what are you doing now?"

"I'm back home. Well, not home, really – my mother and I, we don't see things the same way. I don't know, she just can't cope. I don't suppose I can blame her …"

No? I thought grimly, but I sure could. "Honey, do you want to come down and stay here? I can find a place for you."

"No – but thanks, Peach. No. I want … I want to do something here. I'm going to start a foundation, before I get too sick to do anything. It's to help girls stay away from there, girls just starting the life. I just wanted you to hear it from me, before anyone else starts talking."

I'm not exactly hooked into either the West Coast or Canadian gossip circuits, but I took the remark as she had meant it, as underlining our connection to each other, and as a way of saying good-bye. "Mirra –" I whispered.

"It's at the bank," she said briskly. "The foundation money, they have the fund at the bank. I'll have them get in touch with you. I expect you'll want to make a donation."

"I will," I said, feeling empty and inadequate. After we hung up I sat there for a very long time, silently watching my son.

* * * * * *

We moved to Watertown, Sam started first grade, and life went on. Later that winter I heard that Mirra had died, and yes, I did send some money to her foundation. Poor silly Mirra.

The issue of safety is key in the sex industry. I consistently tell all the women who work for me to be safe, and if I hear that a client has tried to coerce anybody into doing anything she doesn't want to – hell, even if what I hear is that a client has offered extra money for her to have sex without a condom – I cut him off. There are so few ethical stands I can take in my business. That's one of the few I can.

I've lost clients over the issue, and that's fine with me. My girls stay safe.

You'd think, sometimes, that the issue of AIDS had never come up. The arguments I get. The clients who are convinced that if they have the subject out with me just one more time, I'll change my mind. The girls who, absurdly, want to have unsafe sex for more money, because they're young and beautiful and they cannot imagine that anything ugly will ever touch them, defile them, kill them – like Mirra. No, not like Mirra. Not if I can help it.

I remember sending someone on a call to a couple, a husband and wife – Julianna, it was, though the clients knew her as Cherie. The call was a disaster any way you looked at it. The couple had planned it poorly, the wife had obviously been talked into agreeing by her husband, and freaking out once Julianna/Cherie got there. A threesome with the man you love is a great deal more acceptable in the abstract than it is in the flesh, especially when the girl who comes to have sex with your husband is far more beautiful and far younger than you.

Julianna was handling it all okay, though, reassuring the wife, being seductive to the husband, and balancing it all as best she could. She encouraged them to start without her, which of course they did *sans* condom. And then the husband pulled his cock out of his wife's pussy and proposed to put it immediately into Julianna.

She was quick, had a condom to hand immediately, but he was trying to wheedle his way into her without one. She said no, he got insistent, and in the middle of it all the wife started freaking again, seeing her husband attempting to fuck someone else. A disaster, any way one looked at it.

She finally left, with the wife in hysterics and the husband angry as hell. He called me and wanted his money back. I had to tell him in no uncertain terms that under no circumstances could he attempt to have sexual intercourse with any of my girls without her consent, much less without a condom. And all the while I could hear his wife wailing in the background.

Poor Benjamin. He had no idea why I was so unresponsive to him on that particular night.

Madam

* * * * * *

I sat and looked out at the stars. You see them, here. I don't think that I ever saw them when I lived in the city.

Losing the baby was making me think about what I want for Sam, and for Benjamin, and even for myself. And I'm not sure that I want to spend the rest of my life being a madam.

It's easy: that's the seductive part, I suppose. I can do it in my sleep. I can do it without thinking. I know my clients and I know how to handle the women who work for me and I can absorb – to some extent – the pain and crisis that sometimes go along with the job.

The question is whether I want to.

I looked out at the stars for a long time after I turned the phones off for the night. I watched them long enough to see them shift in the night sky. And then I went to bed and wrapped my arms around my husband and dreamed of all the people I had lost.

The next morning after Sam left for school, I called Caro and found out what I needed to do to get a real estate license.

EPILOGUE

I came from a dysfunctional family, and I became a madam. Connection? Probably, although the older I get, the more I realize that a lot of people come from dysfunctional families. Some of them can overcome their past; some can't.

Sam is at school and Benjamin is at work and I'm getting ready to go out and do my very first open house. I'm a little excited, a little nervous, and very happy. As I put the key in the ignition, I'm suddenly overwhelmed by an image of my own past. I think about standing in that hallway, with my father dying on the other side of a closed door and a priceless Chinese vase next to me. It took me a long time to remember breaking that vase. I've wondered for an even longer time what its significance was.

Anger is best expressed, because if you keep it inside, it can poison you for the rest of your life. I showed my anguish in breaking my mother's price-less artifact, in breaking something that I thought she loved more than she loved me – and then I buried that act deep in my subconscious. I didn't remember it until I came close to joining my father, to killing myself.

I told Sam that I plan to change jobs, that I'm tired of the telephone and am studying to sell houses instead. One day last week, he brought home a picture he had done of me surrounded by houses and people with smiles on their faces. So maybe the two profes-sions have something in common: making people happy.

Perhaps by the time Sam is in his teens or in col-lege, sex work will have been legalized. It's the only thing that makes any sense if the country believes – as it claims to do – in the safety of all. But I have my doubts. The sex industry is and will always be, it seems to me, shrouded in mystery: something that both titillates and horrifies. And those of us who par-ticipate in it fascinate and repel at the same time.

At some level, I understand that thinking. At another, I don't. Wars are being waged around the world, children are dying of hunger, and there's still no cure for AIDS. People paying for an hour of pleas-ure seems a small thing next to all of that.

I look at the popularity of television series that feature all sorts of illicit sex, which is apparently okay with middle America – just so long as there's no money exchanged. And I look at all the rest: we apparently don't mind our children being exposed in the media to guns, to cheating, to killing, but God forbid anyone should see a naked breast.

Funny old world we live in.

In the meantime, I've lost so much. My father, some of my friends, my unborn child. I can't stay angry with the world for not understanding me. I can't keep breaking that vase, over and over and over again. I need to look to the light, to the future, to realizing my dreams and raising my son.

That's not such a bad plan for the rest of one's life, now, is it?

Read on for an extract of Jenny Angell's
first book, *CALLGIRL*.

ONE

"Mind the gap ... Mind the gap!" I was standing on a subway platform in London, in the Underground, listening to a disembodied voice telling me in the tones of a not-too-friendly nanny to watch my step. I appreciated the concern, if not its delivery.

So I stood there dutifully minding the gap, and I thought about the newspaper advertisement folded into the shoulder bag I carried. It felt conspicuous, as though everyone else on the train platform could tell exactly what was in there, and what it said.

I had picked up the *Phoenix* just before leaving Boston, on an impulse that wasn't really an impulse but was disguised as one anyway. My impulses usually are. I was in London for a week, lecturing at the London School of Economics, and my mind wasn't exactly on my work.

It should have been, of course. It was an honor and a privilege to be here, and my professional life shouldn't be impacted just because I was having problems in my personal life. But that's the way that it always works, isn't it? You think you can separate it all out, put your life into neat little compartments where nothing overlaps with anything else. You think that, and you're wrong.

My personal life was screaming for attention. Loudly. I needed money. I needed a lot of money, and I needed it quickly.

I needed the money because Peter, my most recent boyfriend, had not only decided to fly to San Francisco to meet up with some ex (whom he had been fucking behind my back the whole time we were together, as it turned out), but had also emptied my checking account before leaving. A prince among men.

Rent was due. The decimated bank account had held all the money I had to live on until the end of the semester. That was when the two community colleges where I taught sociology elective classes would be paying me. I had to live within those parameters, with budgets planned well in advance and no extra or surprise expenses allowed.

Peter's desertion decidedly qualified as a surprise expense.

In any case, the end of the semester was two months off. Which was why I needed a lot of cash.

Madam

I dealt with the crisis in my usual way. I spent one night getting very drunk and feeling very sorry for myself, and I got up the next morning, did what I could to deal with my hangover, and made a list. I love lists, I always have. Lists give me the illusion of being in control. I listed every possible way I could get the money I needed.

It was a depressingly short list.

The one thing I was not going to do was ask for assistance in any way. Not from my family and not from the Commonwealth of Massachusetts. I had been the one to make the bad judgment call, it made no sense to ask anyone else to pay for my mistakes. So even though I had written down the words "government assistance" on my list, I ignored them and moved on.

I frowned at the remaining items, crossed off "childcare," both since I'm really incompetent with children and also the pay was too low to make much of a difference, and frowned again at what was left.

I was going to have to try *one* of these options. I didn't have a lot of choices left. I took a deep breath, and I went to work.

I called a number I had found in some campus newspaper, Boston University or Northeastern or something, the ubiquitous one we've all seen, the one that is looking for people to sit in cubicles and respond to sex chatline calls. Talk sex, convince them that you're hot for them, that sort of thing.

285

Well, the rat bastard boyfriend *had* told me that I had a sexy voice, so I figured it was worth a try. I'd only do it this once, of course.

I clearly hadn't given the idea enough thought, because I was totally unprepared for the sleaziness of my interview. I hadn't imagined ahead of time the really scary visuals: the rows of tiny cubicles, with women sitting in them wearing headsets and talking; they never stopped talking. Lights were flashing on their phones. Mostly they were middle-aged, with sagging flesh and garish makeup and an air of indifference that might have been cruel if it hadn't felt so hopeless.

And I hadn't visualized the way-too-young greasy guy with way too many piercings who never even looked at me as he squeezed words out past a toothpick sticking to his lower lip. His eyes didn't leave the skin magazine he was thumbing through. "Okay, honey. Eight bucks an hour, two calls minimum."

"What does that mean, two calls minimum? Two calls an hour?"

That earned me a glance. I couldn't tell if it was amusement or pity. "Two calls minimum at a *time*."

I stared at him. "You mean keep two different people on the phone …?"

"Yeah, that's right." He sounded bored beyond belief. "If one of 'em wants you to be a Ukrainian gymnast and the other wants you to be a tattooed lesbian, you go with it. Time's money. Want the job?"

I was still stuck imagining the reactions of the clients when you got them mixed up. It was indescribable. Sure. For eight dollars an hour. This could happen.

So I gave up, tore up the list, and panicked again for a while about the money thing. The bills kept coming in, as they have a habit of doing: time stops for no bankruptcy. I could read the official-looking print through the rusted gap in my mailbox: computer-generated, thin envelopes. Some had a strip of red around the edges. No need to open them. I knew what they said.

Suitably enough, one of the classes I was teaching was a sociology elective called *On Death and Dying*. Suitably, of course, because I was accompanying it with such dark thoughts. I would break the class into discussion groups and stare over their heads out the window and feel that cold claw of fear somewhere in my stomach. One of those weeks we talked about suicide.

It didn't sound like such an impossible option.

And then, slowly at first, my thoughts kept going back to the newspaper. I sometimes looked in the *After Dark* section of the *Phoenix*, even after I decided that I couldn't possibly be both a Ukrainian gymnast and a tattooed lesbian, and I wasn't stopping anymore at the chatline number ads.

The next pages, the ones after the telephone lines, were for the escort services.

I'd look, and then I'd shut the paper and let my cat Scuzzy sleep on it while I pretended that it wasn't there, and corrected student essays instead. And yet … and yet.

Why not?

Was it such an impossible idea? Did I really want to add an extra fifty hours a week to my schedule, working at a Borders bookstore or a Starbucks coffeehouse for just over minimum wage? Those were the next options on the list, after all. I'd even interviewed. Borders said I could start any time.

It was around then that a voice in my head started speaking up. It sounded suspiciously like my mother's voice, and the voice was not happy at all about the direction my thoughts were taking. It was interesting that the voice hadn't spoken up when I looked into the sex-on-the-phone idea, but that was another issue altogether. The voice was certainly going into overtime now.

Just wait, I said to the voice. Hold on a moment. Let's think about this. You can sit in a cubicle and pretend to be having sex with two (or more, as seemed to be the assumption) men at once, keeping them on the phone for as long as you can, and having the same conversations twenty or thirty or forty times a night. Or you can do the real thing. Once a night. For a hell of a lot more than eight dollars.

And what's the difference? Honestly?

There's a *huge* difference, the voice responded. It sounded exasperated, as my mother's had when I was disagreeing with her on a moral question. Okay, I said, trying to be open: but why? Where *do* you draw the line? Why is one thing semi-acceptable and the other not at all? You wouldn't exchange sex for five dollars; I'll accept that. But, let's see: would you for five hundred? For five thousand? For five million? Ah, yes, that's a different question, isn't it? So, as Churchill once said, now we know what you are, we just have to determine your price.

The voice had fallen oddly silent. I couldn't blame it: it's hard to talk back to Churchill.

Later on, when I got to know some of the other callgirls, I asked them the same question. Why is having casual sex with a man you pick up in a singles bar considered acceptable, but having sex as a business proposition is not? Which is more ethical? Marie said that what decided her to start working for the service was the moment she stopped and really thought about how many men she had allowed to put their penises inside her, men who later made her skin crawl with disgust – and that for no money at all.

It gives you pause, it really does.

I had let the rat bastard boyfriend touch me, kiss me, fuck me. Now the mere thought of his dick, his hands, his tongue made me feel queasy, dirty somehow.

And in the end, as it turned out, I had paid *him*.

So I picked up the *Phoenix* on my way to Logan Airport and England, and I sat in the student dormitory that was all I could afford for the week I was lecturing there, and I opened the *After Dark* section and read the ads.

I circled one.

* * * * * *

Peach was brisk when we spoke on the telephone. "You can refuse any call if you don't like the sound of the guy, or how it feels," she said. "You can say no to anything that he asks for that you don't want to do, and I'll back you up. The only thing you can't do is steal clients."

"Steal clients?" I must have sounded blank.

"Yeah, slip them your phone number, make a deal with them. Arrange to see them without going through the service. They try it all the time. I've got the regulars pretty much whipped, but they'll always try it with a new girl."

It had never occurred to me to steal clients. The whole point of going through an agency, I had thought, was so that I would be protected by that agency. Okay, so I was still pretty naïve at that point.

She had a little canned, obviously well-rehearsed speech. I tried to take it all in. This business is a crapshoot, sometimes it's okay, sometimes less so.

You've never done this before? That's good: they like that. They like to think that they're the first. Remember: you can say no to anything. One hour exactly. I get sixty dollars, you get the rest. Tips are all yours, but don't get too excited; the eighties are over. No one tips anymore. So why don't you try it out, just one call? Just give me your description and I'll send you out, after that you can decide whether it's something that you want to do again or not.

I could have sworn that somewhere in the narrative she stifled a yawn.

I was far from yawning, myself. I answered with some trepidation, but apparently they were the right answers; apparently I passed whatever internal test I was being subjected to. There was the briefest of pauses when I had finished. "Hmm. All right. I'll have you see Bruce tonight. I know he'll like you."

"Tonight?" For all my eagerness, that seemed very soon. Too real, too fast. Panic set in. "Peach, I'm not dressed up –" I was wearing jeans and a t-shirt, with a black vest and an olive linen jacket over it. Not my image of how a callgirl should dress. (Like I knew anything: I had seen *Pretty Woman* and that film starring Sigourney Weaver as a scholar by day, callgirl by night and that was about it. What you might call a limited frame of reference.)

Besides, how I was dressed was not the only issue here. "You see, I had hoped to meet you in person before I started," I said. You know, like a real interview.

"That's not necessary," she said, her voice brisk. "You can't lie about your description, the guy you see will tell me the truth. I don't need to see you first."

"I want you to," I said, thinking that I was sounding petulant and not knowing what to do about it. I had wanted to come across as – oh, say, at least marginally sophisticated. "I mean, there's no problem, I look young, I look good, but ..." My voice trailed off. Now I was definitely sounding lame. Great interview. Articulate as hell. Try that on one of your classes someday.

Her voice changed subtly. Later, when I got to know Peach, I recognized the slight shift in manner and attitude: the nursery nanny whose charges aren't following directions. Obedience and agreement are expected. Don't tell me you're going to be difficult. "A lot of different women work here," she said. "Our clients have all sorts of tastes. I'm already thinking of one or two who I think you'd enjoy; one's a surgeon, the other is a musician. They're guys who want to talk, guys who'll appreciate you, who don't just want a quick visit." She was being careful, I realized, not to use the s-word, not to be any more specific than she had to be. "I think you'll enjoy spending time with them." Come on, now, children, playtime is over, listen to Nanny.

I said, trying not to sound stubborn or defensive, "I still want to meet you first. I want you to see me. I want to be sure."

Peach was dismissive. "There's no sense in meeting unless you find you like the work, unless you want to keep doing it. And don't worry – you're dressed perfectly. A lot of the clients go for casual. So do it, or not. You decide. Call me at seven, if you want, and I'll set it up."

And that was that. Do it, or not.

I decided to do it.

She was as good as her word. When I called her back she was full of information, delivered at the staccato speed of a submachine gun, and I found myself scribbling on the back of an envelope from my jacket pocket. "His name is Bruce, his number is 555-4629. Your name is Tia – isn't that what you said you wanted to be called? Anyway, you're twenty-six, you weigh 125 pounds, thirty-six, twenty-six, thirty-five. C-cup bra. You're a student. Call him, and then call me back after you've talked to him."

Did she always tell her employees what they were supposed to look like? I wondered. I didn't ask, though, and later found out that, indeed, Peach tailored the precise description to what the client was looking for. Within reasonable bounds, of course. Now, however, I was just reacting to the speed of it all. I said, slowly, "Peach, I called you to say that

I want to try it. How did you get me a client so quickly?"

She laughed. "I had a feeling that you'd say yes. Now call him. Do you remember everything I told you?"

Barely. That was a lot of data, I thought, staring at the envelope. A lot of data that I had never thought about actually articulating to anybody. I remembered a line from *Half Moon Street*: "Don't worry, I'm naked underneath!"

Apparently these were guys who didn't want to take that on faith.

Well, okay. I didn't have any idea what my real measurements were, but those sounded as good as any. I took a deep breath. This was it. I was really doing this.

Bruce asked me to go through the statistics again, but he seemed pleasant enough (I had been expecting stuttering, maybe?) and gave me directions to Revere. To a marina. He lived, it transpired, on a boat.

He was a bear of a man, bearded, with eyes that twinkled behind his glasses. We sat on a small sofa in the cabin of his sailboat, drank a very nice chilled Montrachet, and talked about music, our conversation interspersed with clumsy silences. It felt oddly familiar, as if ... well, to tell you the truth, what it felt like was a date. A first date. A blind date.

An extremely awkward one.

He got up to refill our wineglasses and when he came back he did the little classic pretend yawn and stretch that is a favorite move from everybody's first junior high romance; but at that moment I leaned forward to pick up my glass and so he missed. Oops.

I hadn't done it all that well in junior high, either, come to think of it.

He cleared his throat. "Do you mind if I put my arm around you?"

I was bemused. Did I mind? Um – well, no. I came here for you to fuck me, you're paying two hundred dollars an hour to fuck me, I don't expect I should balk at you putting your arm around me … I looked at him, unable for a moment to respond. He really meant it. It was endearing beyond belief.

I'd imagined a lot of things, back in London. I'd imagined even more since then, sitting alone in the whirlpool at my gym and thinking about what I was about to do. I'd imagined a lot of pretty unimaginable things, to tell the truth. What I could never have imagined was this polite awkward guy asking my permission to put his arm around me.

"That would be nice," I managed to say, and a moment later he kissed me.

Definitely a first date kiss.

I returned it with some enthusiasm, moving my arms up his shoulders and around his neck and drawing him deeper, closer to me, opening my mouth to his and gently sliding my tongue against his teeth.

And it was at that precise moment that I knew it was going to be all right. This wasn't anything esoteric or bizarre or dangerous: this was something I had done before, something I did well, and – best of all – something I enjoyed doing.

He slid his hand up under my t-shirt, raising my bra, and then he was touching my breasts, playing with the nipples as they hardened in response, still with his mouth crushed against mine. I moaned slightly and pressed my body closer to his, and I could feel his heartbeat accelerating, hear his breath coming faster. We pulled away from each other, slightly, responding to some inner common impulse, and his eyes met mine. "You're beautiful," he said.

"Thank you," I whispered, tracing the shape of his lips with my fingertip.

He cleared his throat. "Would you – can we go in the bedroom?"

I knew just what to say; this was easy, after all. I could do this in my sleep, on automatic pilot. I didn't even have to think about anything. It couldn't have felt more natural. "Yes, please," I said, keeping a sense of controlled eagerness in my voice.

The bedroom wasn't far. We were, after all, on a boat.

I had taken the precaution of buying condoms on my way over. Now I hesitated before following him, ostensibly finishing the wine in my glass, and I slipped one from my handbag into my jeans pocket. Nice work. Unobtrusive as hell. Hey, what do you want, I'm new at this.

And it was still feeling like a first date.

The room was illuminated only by the open door to the living space. I could see a bed and little else. It didn't matter; the bed was really all that we needed. I slid out of my jacket and vest, pulled off my t-shirt and bra. I did it slowly, as seductively as I could manage, unhooking the bra behind me and letting it drop to the floor. Bruce was watching me. "You're beautiful," he breathed again, and I smiled and extended a hand to him, suddenly confident of my power, of my attraction. "Come here,"

I said, my voice as low and husky as I could make it.

Marlene Dietrich, eat your heart out.

We ended up sitting on the bed, next to each other, kissing deeply. Later, I learned that some callgirls won't kiss, that they consider their lips the only part of themselves that they can withhold. Even now, I disagree. Maybe the pretense of romance is better than no romance at all. Or maybe I just like to kiss.

He pushed me back on the bed, gently, his head going down to my breast, his mouth on my nipples. I leaned my head back and closed my eyes.

I had thought it was going to be terrible. I was still dealing with the confusion of it being – if anything – pleasant.

I was struggling with the buttons on his flannel shirt, pulling at them, my own breath sounding ragged. I pulled the sides of the shirt apart, ran my hands against his chest, up to his neck, pulling him up to kiss me again, more demanding this time, murmuring something as I did.

There was a moment of awkwardness with the jeans, both his and mine, and then they were off and we were lying next to each other, our hands groping, our bodies pressing together. I could feel his cock hard against my leg, and I sighed again as my fingers crept down and touched it; I could feel the excitement pulsing through it, through him.

He was kissing my neck, running his tongue along my collarbone, his hand holding my breast. I stroked his cock, gently, firmly, feeling all of his body straining against me. I moaned softly, my fingertips light on him, his inner thighs, his curly hair, his cock, his balls. I felt myself getting wet, felt my pelvis straining to be closer to him, and it was he who, to my surprise, pulled himself up on an elbow. "Do you have any protection with you?"

Wow. Either this was the nicest man in Boston, or else Peach really did have him trained. "In my pocket," I said, gesturing at the clothes on the floor.

"Do you mind?" He picked my jeans out of the pile and handed them to me, immediately going back to kissing my neck. I fumbled for the condom package, and he took it from me.

I sat up then and leaned down to touch his cock with my lips. Yeah, I know, I know, you shouldn't do anything without protection, what can I say, he wasn't all that close to coming, and I was trying to show him that I liked him. Even then, I was thinking about repeat business.

I was already understanding, if only at an intuitive level, the credo of every callgirl. Regular clients are our bread and butter, the reason that we can keep doing what we do. Finding someone like Bruce and making sure that he asks for us, over and over again.

I hadn't thought about how Peach had gotten him so easily for me, for my first night. Later, I found out that she had an arrangement with Bruce, that he saw new callgirls. Instead of him calling her, she called him. Everybody won: Bruce got the thrill of initiating a first-timer, the girl got an easy call. At the time, however, I was just feeling lucky, feeling like this wasn't going to be so awful and tedious a job, after all.

All the questions – is it wrong to like my work? Am I supposed to hate working for a service? – came later. At that moment, I was just glad that I could do it, that it wasn't unpleasant, and that I was good at it.

I licked up and down his cock while he opened the condom package. He paused from time to time to pull my hair back from my face so that he could watch me, watch his cock sliding in and out of my mouth, between my lips, and he sighed. "God, you're good."

I moved back so that he could slip on the condom. He kissed me while he was doing it, our tongues touching; he was still sighing with pleasure. And then I was leaning back on the bed and he was on top of me, his big body over mine, his hardness sliding inside me, and I opened my legs to him, wrapped my legs around him to pull him in deeper, and he sighed again, even louder.

I kissed his neck as he started to thrust inside me, and then I gripped his shoulders and took his thrusts, his cock big and hard inside me, his beard rough against my cheek. At one point I thought I heard him say "Tia." I wasn't quite sure, but I said "Bruce," and that seemed to please him. He moaned again and thrust even harder.

I could feel us both sweating, even though it was only March, and I had been chilly when I got there. The portholes were open, but it wasn't the lack of air that was making me so hot, making us so hot together. I slid my hands up over the hair on his chest as he continued to move inside me, and tightened my hands around his shoulders again – they almost slipped off from his sweat.

He came suddenly, just as I was grabbing his hair and pulling his face down to kiss me again. He groaned and his whole body shuddered; I pulled him against me and held him tightly. "I'm here, baby," I whispered. "I'm here."

Can I tell you this now? It was better sex than I'd had with the rat bastard boyfriend. Ever. And – best of all – I was getting paid for it.

And it got better. There was none of the postcoital abruptness I usually associate with one-night stands. He rolled off me and pulled me over to him, my head on his chest, listening to the thudding of his heart. I continued to caress him, gently, my fingertips playing lightly over his chest. I blew gently on the sweat, and he shivered and tightened his arm around me. Better, on the whole, than any other one-night encounter I'd ever had.

Bruce disappeared into the bathroom and was dressed first, but had wine waiting when I emerged from the bedroom, and he kissed my cheek as he handed it to me.

The telephone rang. He picked it up, said, "Yeah, Tia's here, hang on a minute," and passed the receiver over to me. "For you."

I was puzzled. "Hello?"

It was Peach. "All set?"

"Yes." I had no idea what she meant.

"Okay, good, call me when you get out." She must have sensed that I didn't understand. She sighed. "I always call when the hour's up. Some guys play games. Sometimes they try to make you stay longer. He pays for your time, and I make sure that he gets what he paid for. And that you get out safely, that you're not stuck or stranded or anything like that. So leave now, and call me from a pay phone."

"Okay." I handed the telephone back to Bruce. He obviously knew the drill: he had the money in his hand already. "I really liked meeting you, Tia."

I smiled as I slid the bills into my jacket pocket. "It was nice meeting you, too, Bruce. I hope I can see you again."

"I'd like that a lot." He even sounded like he meant it.

He escorted me off the gangway, kissed me again on the cheek, gave me a brief hug. "Good-night."

"Good-night, Bruce." And I walked away toward my car; I felt like singing, or skipping, something joyous and happy. I had just spent a pleasant evening. After I took out the sixty dollars that was Peach's fee, I had made one hundred and forty dollars. In one hour.

Anybody else out there making that kind of money?

I called her from the first pay phone I spotted; she asked politely how it had gone, and wished me a good night.

I hung up the telephone and was struck by an incongruous thought. I remembered sitting in that whirlpool at the health club, and feeling grateful that I had the lifetime membership (a gift, ironically enough, from my mother), so that I would always be able to go there. I was grateful that they were open late at night. I remembered sitting there and thinking, when I start working, I'll come and sit here and let all the bad feelings soak away with these bubbles. I'll use this place to feel clean again.

I was smiling broadly as I got back in my car to drive home. There was nothing that I needed to cleanse myself from. What bad feelings?

I slept really well that night. No nightmares, no waking up sweating with the panic pressing in on me, no knots in my stomach. I was gainfully employed. I even wrote a check to the electric company.

This was going to work. And I wasn't even shocked that there weren't any bad feelings at all.

TWO

The next day dawned, as next days inevitably – and depressingly – do. I had showered when I got home, and did it again out of habit before getting dressed and heading out for class. I dressed in community college attire, which (per my definition, anyway) means professional enough to be able to be distinguished from the students and not so formal as to make people think that one is taking oneself too seriously. In the world of academia, community colleges are certainly not to be taken too seriously. That's unfortunate and not even very accurate; but wasn't it Lenin who said that perception is reality? It's where a lot of people start – and where a lot of people finish up, too.

I didn't want to think about that.

I was fortunate in my *Death and Dying* class. It was being offered as a partnership agreement between the college and a local hospital, and was largely populated by registered nurses going back to school to acquire a Bachelor of Science in Nursing. So there was not only a lot of motivation among the students, there was also a lot of expertise. I was talking about death: my students were people who dealt with it every time they went to work. It was more than a little humbling.

That first morning after working for Peach, though, I have to admit that I wasn't feeling particularly humble. I was feeling high.

That day we were talking about death and war. It was one of my favorite classes on the syllabus, because there was so much material with which to challenge the students. I didn't want to tell them whether war was right or wrong; I wanted to challenge their perceptions and help them come to their own conclusions. Or their own confusion. Either was acceptable.

I read two poems aloud – Edna St. Vincent Millay's "The Conscientious Objector," and Randall Jarrell's "Losses," both of them highly emotional, exquisitely beautiful, and extremely challenging. I read the poems as I always did, not really reading but reciting them by heart. I was watching the class, looking for reactions that I could use in the discussion that was going to follow. And then, suddenly, for a scary split second – it honestly was no more than that – I was back on the boat, sitting and sipping wine after getting dressed, having a packet of money pressed into my hand.

And I liked it. As though seeing it all in fast-motion, I stepped back from where I was standing, stepped out of my body and looked at myself, and I liked what I saw. I liked my professional competence, the fact that I was teaching something important and teaching it well. And I also liked the secret knowledge that the night before I had been paid to be sexy, beautiful, desirable. I liked both sides of myself. I liked them a lot.

These people, my students, listened to poetry that they fiercely believed had no place in their lives, simply because I had asked them to. I had built up a measure of trust with them over the weeks and months of this course so that I could ask them to listen to archaic words and find the truths spoken through them. They trusted me. I was an authority figure.

In fact, half of the class called me "Doctor." The authority figure to the fore. It was a little scary. What if I was too much of an authority figure to be sexy? What if I couldn't do another call for Peach? What if I went on a call and got rejected? What if Bruce had been an exception? What if I really was too old for all this? Would I end up remembering that first night and becoming bitter because I had glimpsed something that I wanted and couldn't have? Wouldn't it have been better, if that were to be the case, to never have started at all?

So when I called Peach later that afternoon, I told her once again – and somewhat more firmly – that I wanted to meet her in person.

She didn't like it. She fought it. As I would find out later, she never liked meeting any of the girls, not at first. Sometimes not ever. She always waited until she had already formed an opinion of them through the telephone, through reports from the clients. I never knew why. Maybe seeing them would make the whole endeavor too real to her. Maybe she could keep some distance as long as both her employees and her clients remained disembodied voices on the other end of a telephone line.

But the reality – the necessary reality of her job – was that she sent some girls, knowingly, into some pretty awful places, and some even more awful situations. She had to. As she said to me once, in a curiously unguarded moment, "Jen, if I ever really thought about it, I could never send anyone anywhere." I think that maybe her job was easier for her if she didn't have to visualize them, feel that she had really encountered them, acknowledged them as individuals. At the end of the phone, a girl could be a list of statistics and lies: her measurements, her height and weight, the color of her eyes, the length of her hair, her approximate age. Add an invented abbreviated history ("She's sweet, just moved here from Kansas to go to school."), all the information adapted and re-adapted, tailored afresh for each client. And the clients were consistently (and, I thought at first, a little naïvely) surprised that Peach could meet their specifications so exactly.

A brief aside, a matter of mild interest: here's a fact: Men can't guess a woman's age. There has to be some brain cell in men that doesn't activate, some deficit encoded in male DNA, this inability to look at a woman and make reasonable chronological conclusions about her. Or maybe it's just a result of intense sexual arousal, when, as we all know, only one head is fully functional. But in any case, they can't tell how old a woman is. Especially if she's already given them a number.

I was a few months away from turning thirty-four when I started working for the agency, but Peach's assistant Ellie immediately took care of that.

The day after my first call with Bruce, I spoke with Peach when I called to confirm that I was available that evening. As it turned out, Peach herself wasn't. "It's my night off, I'm going out," she said. "Don't worry, I told my assistant Ellie about you, she'll be talking to you shortly." It made me a little nervous, but I had psyched myself up – and my bank account was reminding me that it wasn't the moment yet to take a night off. Besides, if I chickened out now, I might never call again. I was on a roll. I had to take advantage of it.

Ellie was working the phones and called me around seven to take notes. She needed my general description, hopefully to connect it with a client's request; and she asked me my age. Her reaction was direct and no-nonsense. "No way. No one wants to see someone who's over thirty," she said. I tried to tell her the number didn't matter. I tried to explain that at work I was always mistaken for an undergraduate rather than a faculty member. I might have been thirty-three, but I didn't look it.

Apparently the number mattered to Ellie. "These guys have no idea what anything over thirty looks like, they're morons with only one thing in their little pea brains." Ellie, as I was to discover, had a cynical view of the clientele. And, come to think of it, of life, too. "Even twenty-eight, twenty-nine, that's pushing it, way old to them. I can't get you a call if I tell them you're thirty-three."

"Okay." I wasn't going to argue. She knew more about it than I did. New game, new rules, I was willing to learn. I later found out that Ellie, herself, had only just turned twenty.

She was still talking. "We'll say you're twenty-four, that way you can be in grad school, the intellectual thing is a turn-on for some of these guys. You'll be great with the smart ones; they're always asking for someone who's in school."

Worked for me. Got me a client that night, in fact, a soft-spoken engineer from New Delhi. And after that, Peach generally told clients that I was anything from twenty-two to twenty-nine, depending on who the guy was and what he wanted. I thought that twenty-two was a little over the top, but none of the men I saw ever questioned the veracity of what she said.

I have to say, though, that in spite of my confidence in my looks, I *was* a little spooked by the age issue. After all, the common perception of prostitutes is that they are young, even underage sometimes, the cheerleader sort. If they were of the *femme fatale* type, it was always on the Lolita end of the spectrum. I had seen *Pretty Woman*, okay? She was young, young enough to still be idealistic, as the movie was quick to point out. I'd also seen *Half Moon Street*, but it was careful to indicate that Sigourney Weaver's age and intelligence were the exception, that even her clients weren't initially sure she was what they wanted. Julia Roberts' character – young, hip, fast-talking, and sweet – was the conventional norm. The hooker with the heart of gold.

I was not young, hip, fast-talking, or sweet, and I had no illusions about the state of my heart. I wasn't going to fit into the mold. That made me uneasy. After Peter the Rat Bastard, I really didn't need another rejection.

The funny thing is that when I think about all the processing, all the thinking, all the planning that I did when I was starting out, there was never a moment when I doubted that I could do this. I sat in the dormitory in London staring at my notes for the following morning's lecture, and I felt nervous about how the lecture would go over in another culture, what sort of questions people would be asking me, that sort of thing. I sat there feeling nervous, and even then half of my brain was rehearsing the lecture and the other half was considering whether or not to become a prostitute. It was an odd juxtaposition, and yet I never for one moment wondered whether I *could*.

I just knew. I knew that I was pretty, but my confidence really didn't have a lot to do with that. It was more along the lines of knowing that I was powerful. I had had a succession of boyfriends – and, let's be honest here, girlfriends too – before the rat bastard, and they all claimed that I was the best lover they'd ever had. Well, okay, maybe you've heard that too, perhaps they were just saying what they thought I wanted to hear. I'm willing to consider the possibility. I'll grant you that they didn't all mean it.

But you *know* it when you're good at something, really good, you know it viscerally, in your muscles and your cells and your blood, at some non-rational and yet absolutely certain level. I knew I was good at sex, at romance, at seduction. It was something innate, something I didn't think about. When I was flirting with a man I went into automatic pilot. I just did. I didn't think. I flirted. And I always got him. Whomever I wanted, I got.

It was just my bad judgment that I had once wanted the rat bastard.

Once preliminaries were aside, I was confident of my power. I knew that once I had a man – any man – alone in a room with our clothes off, I would please him. I could make him crazy, make him ecstatic, make him want more and more and more. I knew that there is a certain sexiness about experience and education, that I had something to offer that the twenty-year-olds did not.

That was why I had circled Peach's ad in the first place. I had been dazed by the array of pictures of silicone-enhanced breasts and blonde women with pouting lips claiming, "I want you in my hot cunt now!" But there among them were the two advertisements that Peach ran. One was for the clients, and it was simple: "Avanti," it declared, in a medium-sized box with a lace border. "When you want more than just the ordinary."

Well, okay, so that could mean anything. But there wasn't any silicone, either, which had to be a good sign.

The other ad, presented on another page in the same typeface, was looking for help: "Part-time work available to complement your real life," it said. "Some college required." That was what got me. No one else mentioned college. This agency had clients who wanted education, clients who presumably wanted to talk intelligently with their escorts, who were looking for something beyond firm breasts and empty thoughts.

These were the clients I wanted to see, men who would view my graduate degrees as enhancing my sexuality rather than detracting from it. This was a possibility.

It was the only one I circled. I sometimes wonder what I would have done if it hadn't worked out. Would I have returned to the ads, found another one to try, one that was less offensive than the others? I don't know.

I took the paper with me to London and the name Avanti sat in the back of my brain while I talked to lecture-halls of students for four days.

I got home, and before I even unpacked I called Peach. And that was the day she sent me to see Bruce.

And so I found that there were people willing to see me – Bruce, the Indian engineer, a legislative aide from the state house; but I was still intensely unsure of my place in a youth-dominated profession. I pressed her again. Just to be sure that "the professor" could fit into her world, that Bruce and the others hadn't been total aberrations.

I guess that by then she figured I was worth the investment of her time. A few days after I saw the legislative aide, she agreed to meet. "All right. What about lunch on Thursday, Legal Seafoods restaurant at Copley, one o'clock?" Rapid decision, rapid planning; it was all so typical Peach.

My palms were sweating. "Okay, great, I'll be there."

I was there. She wasn't. She managed, in point of fact, to avoid me for a week. She didn't go to Legal Seafoods; when I called her at two she had some excuse about a sprained ankle. I, in the meantime, was overdressed even for a downtown mall in a short business suit, had been on my feet in uncomfortable heels for the past hour, and had spent that time nervously scrutinizing every woman who walked in the door in case it was Peach. I was exhausted.

She cancelled two more appointments with me, fortunately with somewhat more notice. I had already paid a teaching assistant I knew from graduate school to cover my class for one of the appointments. I really couldn't keep doing this, letting a potential job screw up what was, after all, my real career. And her choices of venue were never convenient: it was a fair commute to get downtown from my studio apartment in Allston, and then I needed time to find a place in the parking garage and time to locate the restaurant and start guessing which person could be her.

I was beginning to seriously think it wasn't going to happen. It was as though the time spent on the boat with Bruce had been nothing but an image, a snapshot, something so fleeting that it was hardly worthy of the memory. The Indian engineer that Ellie had sent me to see hadn't counted, not really: I had been with him for twenty minutes, tops, and I don't think that he looked at my face once. The guy at the State House had been more interested in the daring aspect of his act than in whom he was doing it with. So I didn't have a lot of experience to draw from.

At the same time, I was also slowly becoming obsessed with the concept of prostitution. My brief brush with it seemed to have sucked me into a well of curiosity – or was it just the researcher in me, the academic? I had started reading about prostitution and was constantly thinking about it.

But I couldn't even manage to meet with my own madam.

I finally was instructed to go to another Legal Seafoods restaurant, this one in the Prudential Mall, and I went, resigned to being blown off again. I didn't even bother dressing up; there seemed to be no point to it. I was wearing my usual at-home uniform of jeans, a sweatshirt, my Ryka sneakers.

I had a plan this time: I was going to wait fruitlessly for her, call her number and collect yet another improbable excuse, and then I was going to spend the afternoon at the Boston College library. I was dressed for it, rather than for her. This time I was prepared, and I had at least brought work to do while I was in town. I wasn't going to waste precious time that could be spent constructively. I had gotten a little jaded by then. I didn't believe for a moment that Peach would keep the appointment.

She did.

She was anything but what I expected. I had been eyeing the brittle, mannequin-like women one sees downtown in Boston, the products of hours spent in the spas and shops of Newbury Street. I assumed she would look like one of them, those women who wear clothes like a challenge, like an armor.

My friend Irene and I had sat once and giggled about them, feeling quite complacent in our assumed superiority. They fell into two categories, we'd decided. Some of them were wealthy non-working wives in from the suburbs for their weekly dosage of collagen, hairspray, and gossip, trying to convince themselves by this contact with the city that their lives in Andover or Acton or southern New Hampshire had meaning and beauty. The others were middle-management professionals, women from the banks and high-rise offices surrounding the Prudential. These women looked perfect because they had to; it was the unwritten agreement in their job descriptions. (Well, maybe it was the unwritten agreement in the suburban wives' job descriptions, too, for all I know.) They had less leisure, less time: they hurried into the mall at lunchtime to buy a birthday gift or a necklace to wear on their power-date after work.

We giggled about it, Irene and I; but there was truth in our observations. These were the women who *were* downtown Boston. And so of course I thought that Peach would look like them. You don't get any more "downtown" than a madam, after all.

God knows I had tried to imagine her. Peach's voice was light, but intense: she was a woman who made quick decisions and usually stood by them – until somebody like me made her change her mind. She had started her own business, and had run it for the past eight years; so perhaps the suits weren't so far off. But her business was seduction and pleasure: the softer fabrics of the women from North Andover and Manchester-by-the-Sea might be more her style. Which way would she go?

There was a voice at my elbow. "Jen? Are you Jen?"

I hadn't even seen her coming. She was my age, give or take a few years – she had to be, to have been in business that long, and have gone to school; it seemed obvious that anyone who required an education from her employees certainly had one herself. She had long thick red hair, a pale face, and tremendous green eyes. She would have looked as though she had just stepped out of a Rossetti painting were it not for her khakis and leather jacket. The pre-Raphaelites, if I remember correctly, favored ethereal white gauzy dresses instead.

I offered my hand, and she hesitated before shaking it. "Hi, yeah, I'm Jen, you must be Peach." Another scintillating remark brought to you by the professor.

"Let's go sit outside," Peach suggested. So much for lunch.

We sat on a concrete wall in the sun and wind, and she came right to the point. "Are you a police officer?"

I stared at her. "Um – no. That was why I called you …"

She was calm. "I just have to make sure. You are not a police officer?"

"No. Do I look like one?"

"Fine, then," she said, and we went on from there.

I wish that all of life could be that simple.

* * * * * *

Okay, so here is what you learn. The Gospel According to Peach. I don't know whether it's true or whether it's one of those cherished urban legends, one specific to activities outside the law. In any case, the common understanding is that if you ask a person if he or she is a police officer, and he or she answers "no," but in fact *is* a police officer, then any subsequent arrest won't stand up in court. It still sounds odd to me; but Peach knew her stuff, so I assume that she knew about that, too.

She wasn't one for small talk. She even had a canned speech for this part, too. "If you ever, ever have any suspicions or bad feelings about a client, don't do the call. There are a couple of ways out of it. If you think it might be a setup, ask if he's a police officer. If you really are suspicious, then say you think you left your keys in the car, you'll be right back, and just get out. If it can wait a few minutes, then when you call me to check in, ask me if your sister called."

I was bemused. "My sister wouldn't call you."

"Doesn't matter," she said impatiently. "It's a code. Hang up and tell the client that I heard from your sister whose husband is much worse, he's in the hospital, and you have to go. Say you're sorry, tell him to call me back, that I'll take care of him. And then leave. I'll talk with you before I take his call so I know what's going on. Never, ever do a call that doesn't feel right. Trust your instincts."

Think what you will, her system worked. No one from her agency ever was arrested, the whole time that I worked for her.

So we met, and she reassured me that I was attractive enough and young enough (at least in appearance) to make it in her profession, and I went home a little bemused and oddly self-confident. Months later, she would tell me that she had felt intimidated by me at that first meeting, that she saw me as clever, sophisticated, and educated and that scared her; but of course at that time I didn't know that. All that I was aware of then – blissfully – was that I had passed muster.

The reality, like it or not, is that we are all governed by the dictates of Madison Avenue, by the excesses of

Hollywood. No matter how much we want to say that it isn't true, it is. If you say that you aren't influenced by Gap posters or twenty-something television programs, if you say that you never compare yourself to them and wonder in your heart of hearts whether you measure up, then I'm sorry: you're simply not telling the truth. *Newsweek* talks about youth culture as though it were a distant phenomenon, to be studied anthropologically; but I guarantee you that the reporters working on the study are concerned about belonging to the very group that they write about.

Take me. I had earned two master's degrees and a difficult doctorate. I was living independently and reasonably happily. I was embarking on a career that I had wanted desperately for all of my life. And yet, that afternoon, I got more pleasure out of the assurance that I was young enough, thin enough, pretty enough, seductive enough to be able to work for an escort service, to hold my own along with twenty-year-olds, than I did out of all of my real, important accomplishments.

So maybe I'm not so smart after all.

* * * * * *

I didn't work that night after meeting Peach. I gave myself permission, instead, to invest in my new job, to fashion and create and slip into my new persona.

I went to my health club and stayed there for three hours, sweating and straining on the Stairmaster and in the weight room, then rewarding myself with twenty minutes in the whirlpool. I chose a Stairmaster machine next to a woman I knew casually from the gym. She worked for one of the software companies out on Route 128. We saw each other once in a great while outside of the club, but mostly our conversations took place as we were panting and watching our heart rates. We told each other about our love lives, or the lack thereof, depending on what was happening at the time. "Want to come to a barbeque tomorrow night?" Susan asked, her eyes on the glowing red dots of the program monitor in front of her.

I hesitated, then replied. "I can't."

That piqued her interest. "Oh, my God, you didn't tell me, that's so cool, Jen, are you *seeing* someone? See, I told you! I knew you'd get over that loser Peter."

"Nothing like that." I paused to swallow some water from my bottle. I couldn't help my thought, I couldn't help but imagine what she would say if I told her the truth. No, Susan, it's not really a date; only sort of. How shocked would you be if I told you what I was really going to be doing? That my date will end with him paying me two hundred dollars? I stifled the laughter that bubbled up with the thought.

I couldn't even imagine what she'd think. *If* she believed me. That was a big if. "I just need money, I'm doing some tutoring."

"That's cool." She was focused again on her hill-climbing pattern. "I need to do something like that."

I smiled my Inner Secret Smile and asked, innocently if a little breathlessly (well, I *was* on a Stairmaster), "Why? I thought you high-tech geeks made all the money."

"Yeah, but tutoring, at least you meet someone who's not a cubicle rat. I'd just like to occasionally have a conversation with someone who has some social skills."

Well, yeah, I thought, the ones I'm seeing aren't all geeks. The social skills part, I wasn't so sure about yet.

After showering and drinking some fruit juice at the club bar, I headed out to make some additions to my wardrobe. Nothing fancy, just as far as the Citibank card would allow me to go. New job, new clothes, my mother always used to say. I had a picture of her, the first day at the bank where she was an assistant vice-president, her hat just so and her gloves matching her shoes and ... well, different times, different wardrobe.

I went to Cacique and bought matching sets of underwear. Not knowing what might lie ahead, I added a few loose camisoles, lacy tops that could work as either lingerie or real clothes. And then of course there were the dreaded and *de rigeur* garter belt and stockings; I was hoping that I'd not have to use them too frequently.

Why, you ask? Here's an insight for the gentlemen in the audience: if a woman ever says that she's comfortable in those things, she's lying. She may be lying to be nice to you, because she knows how much that whole outfit turns you on: but she is lying nevertheless. So appreciate her. A lot.

I, on the other hand, was being paid for it. That makes a little discomfort a lot more comfortable.

I went to a couple more shops, buying clothes that were only slightly more risqué than those I normally wore: slightly shorter skirts, slightly more revealing shirts, that sort of thing. Lots of black. A small black beaded handbag. Clothing in layers, easy to take off, easy to put on – the cramped quarters in the bow of Bruce's boat/bedroom had taught me something about that.

And then I went to a salon and had my hair shaped and blown dry, over-tipped the stylist, and went home. It was ten o'clock. I had a class at two the next day, and was prepared to start my new job in earnest immediately after.

A tale of two careers. I grinned to myself. It doesn't get much better than this.

THREE

The fact is, it was prostitution. You can dress it up however you'd like; but for me to tell myself that earning my living as a prostitute was a situation that couldn't get any better was at best a little naïve. At worst, a little delusional.

After meeting Peach, I had a week and a half of a remarkably ordinary life. Ordinary classes, ordinary calls through Avanti with remarkably ordinary sex.

I'm not sure what I had been expecting – whips and chains, perhaps? Or nun's habits, or something? What I got instead was the sort of unmemorable sex that invariably characterizes first encounters. A little clumsy, a little awkward, and the thought occurring midway through that perhaps you don't really like this person all that much after all.

It happens in real life all the time.

Of course, my situation had a certain advantage over real life. I could leave after an hour. In real life, you're stuck with him for somewhat longer.

A lot of the clients told me what to do, which I found a little off-putting. I've never dealt too well with being told what to do. Not in real life, anyway. It didn't matter: in this context it was acceptable. They got off on it. Sit here, do this, take that off. Do that again. Do it harder. Do it some more. Stand up, kiss me here, turn around, bend over.

Maybe nobody listened to them in real life. Maybe this was the only power they ever felt.

There was a guy out in the suburbs, up in North Andover, a handsome middle-aged African-American who I saw from time to time. After a semi-successful three quarters of an hour spent on his bed, he would make out a check (previously cleared with Peach, of course; this tends to be a cash-only business), always with something of a flourish. He winked at me as he added on the comment line that it was for "purchase of art work." I guess that I qualified.

There was a ridiculously young man in South Boston, nice, who offered me a light beer and then never gave me a chance to drink it.

There was my first hotel client, a regular who visited Boston once a month on business. He was very busy, he informed me, gesturing toward the open laptop on the coffee table with papers scattered all around it. He was as good as his word, too, loudly encouraging me through an energetic blow-job, offering a ten-dollar tip on top of the agency fee after I'd finished. I was out of there in just under twenty minutes. It was eight-thirty at night, I was well-dressed and feeling attractive, walking down a hotel corridor, with one hundred and fifty dollars that I had made in less time than it had taken me to get dressed.

I had been firm with Peach when she called me with the hotel job. I had this idea of guys just passing though Boston, sitting in a hotel, looking up an escort service, maybe not being as careful as they should be. The one thing, I knew, that would bring me back down to earth with a resounding thud would be for me to get arrested. I was willing to have sex so that I could make a living. I wasn't willing to give up my real career, however, and an arrest would do that in a heartbeat. "I only want regulars," I told her. "I only want to see guys that you know."

"It's okay, Matt's a regular," she said, her voice comforting. "He's fine, he's been with us for over a year."

"Okay." I hesitated. "But, Peach, just for the record – I never want to see a new client. Ever. I just can't take that chance."

"Oh, honey," she said. "I understand."

There was the client in Brookline Village who extended his time to a second hour, and used the extra time to take me out for Chinese food after we'd had sex. Very sweet. Double the money, and an expensive dinner with someone I probably would not have chosen to date under different circumstances – but not altogether unpleasant.

Certainly not as unpleasant as some of the dates I'd been on in the past.

None of these men had a particularly scintillating personality. Most of them were, to be honest, incredibly unmemorable. One of them was gruff and pushy. Another kept following up his remarks with, "Oh, you probably don't understand that. Like, who am I talking to here, Einstein or something?" I was new to the profession; I let that one get to me and couldn't suppress a response. "True," I agreed, the third time he said it. "Einstein's doctorate wasn't in anthropology; mine is." He was pretty much quiet, after that.

But the reality is that, all in all, they weren't bad people. Ordinary, marginally attractive, with questionable social skills, yes. Dull, predictable, full of insecurities that they projected onto me, sure. They weren't unfamiliar, or scary, or detestable. I had dated men just like them, in the past, and for no compensation.

One Thursday – about one month after I'd started working regularly for Peach, doing about three or four calls a week – I was nearing the end of the *On Death and Dying* semester. This was my favorite time of all, a time to see what issues I had raised, what ideas I had sparked, what creativity I had unleashed. From the beginning of the semester, students knew that part of their grade would come from a final project, to be done either individually or as part of a group, something that had gripped them, interested them, brought out their passion. I saw amazing things, when projects were presented.

I was not disappointed on this Thursday.

Karen, one of the few students in the class who was not in the nursing program, had done a project on her own. She had gone to a hospice and interviewed dying AIDS patients, recording the interviews on tape. While she talked with them, Karen – who was a professional artist – drew their portraits (all of which she later gave to the subjects, a generous gesture that was a whole story in itself).

I don't think that there was a person in that room who was not mesmerized by what was happening in front of them. The voices on the tape filled the space around us, strong and frightened, peaceful and angry ... We listened to their words and stared at these achingly beautiful faces, these haunted eyes, these hollowed cheeks. I looked around the room, seeing tears, seeing entranced attention, seeing compassion, and my own heart swelled.

Then – how can I make sense of this? – in this wonderful, sacred moment, suddenly my mind flashed back to the night before, to the apartment in Chestnut Hill and the sleek Scandinavian furniture and the guy who was saying, "You teach a class about *death*? Man, that's hot! Death's the best aphrodisiac of all!"

I pushed the image away immediately and blocked it out fast, shocked by its intrusion into this moment. I listened to a man talk about losing his friends, about having his mother afraid to touch him, and my cheeks were flaming. In the midst of this important moment, while doing exactly what I knew that I had been born to do, I had left. I had left as surely as if I had opened the door and gone through it. I had betrayed Karen's beautiful work, and I had betrayed myself.

I didn't know what to do with that knowledge.

I didn't want to think about it.

I tried to forget it.

* * * * * *

That night, if you believe in direct punishment immediately after a misdeed, you would be vindicated. I was punished. I went on a call to Back Bay.

Boston's Back Bay is old brownstones, old families, old money. They are like the apartments of Paris and Budapest – inherited, not sold, and certainly never rented.

It is Commonwealth Avenue at its tree-lined, sweeping best, not the Comm. Ave. I lived near in Allston, with the sound of the creaky Green Line train and the Hispanic markets and the Russian pharmacies. This was Comm. Ave. down near the Public Gardens, where it was modeled on Haussman's boulevards in Paris and almost makes one believe that one is there.

It is Beacon Street, with twisted wrought iron fences and staircases and balconies; it is Marlborough Street, with fanlights over heavy oaken doorways.

It is gaslights on corners and the quiet swish of traffic sounds coming up from Storrow Drive.

You walk along those streets and you wonder about who lives behind the mullioned windows, behind the thick velvet draperies. You imagine that it must be people of culture, people who discuss Rimbaud and Verlaine – or Hofstadter and Minsky – over snifters of brandy on a winter's night.

And, to be honest, I did have some small margin of experience, at least with Beacon Street in the Back Bay. While I was still doing my doctoral coursework I had spent a couple of semesters as a teaching assistant for a professor who lived there, and it was to his apartment that I frequently delivered corrected term papers. The apartment was long and dark, the walls covered with huge dismal oil paintings framed in thick gold gilt frames, each frame nearly touching the next, so that you could barely discern the wallpaper behind them. The rugs were hand-made Orientals, the furniture heavy and mahogany, the books all bound in leather. He gave me tea sometimes, a delicate blend that I couldn't identify, and that I have never tasted since.

So when Peach sent me to Beacon Street, I felt nothing but a sense of mild anticipation. The guy wasn't particularly pleasant on the telephone when I called to set it up, but by then I was amassing my own wisdom about such things. That wisdom said that in general the clients who were the most obnoxious on the telephone were the least so in person, and vice-versa.

Well, so I was wrong about that, too.

But I was still operating from that framework when I talked to him, so I was taking the whole conversation with a grain of salt.

"So, what do you like?"

In my short time in the business, I had already developed an aversion to that question. The point was never what *I* liked, but rather what the client liked, and sometimes this opening felt like an exam, a trick question, a way to get me to say something that he could then pick apart. I was starting to understand clients' minds, you see.

I cleared my throat. "I like lots of things. I'm sure that I'll like you. Why don't I come over, and we'll see how it feels together?"

It was a fourth-floor apartment, one of the apartments that directly overlook the Charles River, and as soon as I got there I moved toward the window with an exclamation of delight. Most guys appreciate that, you complimenting their place. And this was truly magnificent.

All around me, below me, the darkness was punctuated by pinpoints of dazzling brightness, windows spilling out warm yellow light into the night, the flashing red lights on the roofs of the buildings across the river, sparkling unknown reflections in the dark water itself.

The client – Barry by name – wasn't paying me to enjoy the view. I know this to be true because he said so, even as he grasped my arm and pulled me away from the window and toward him, a grasp that was to leave clear deep imprints of his fingers on my bruised skin later.

That first kiss bruised my mouth, too.

He was pinning me against a brick wall and it was uneven, cutting into my back, and it hurt. And his hands hurt, too, pushing against me, squeezing my breasts – hard, too hard. I gasped and pulled away, as far as I could, told him to stop, and he laughed, he actually laughed. "You don't tell me to do anything," he said. "You're just a whore. You hear that? *You* do what *I* say."

I probably should have left then. I had that option; Peach wouldn't have been happy about it, although she would have supported me. I was still feeling my way in the profession, still in my heart of hearts wondering if I really could do it. I still had something to prove.

So I thought, okay, I can handle this. It's only an hour. I can do this for an hour.

He pushed me through an arched doorway into an extremely small bedroom, the bed unmade, a slight undefinable unpleasant odor in the air. There was track lighting, all of it pointing to the bed. A class act, all the way.

He hadn't taken his hands off me once – squeezing, pinching, mauling. He was taking my clothes off and ripped two of the buttons at the neckline to the dress. When I tried to get a modicum of control back, saying that I'd take off my clothes, he grabbed a handful of my hair and shoved his face to within a half-inch of mine. "Shut up, whore!"

Oddly enough, he took a moment to spread towels on the bed. With the mess that the room was already in, the gesture seemed a little ominous.

You probably won't believe this, but the truth is that I don't really remember exactly what happened next. Everything happened so fast, everything became such a blur of pain and fear, that I cannot fashion the experience into words, into a coherent narrative.

Here's what I remember. I remember being pushed down onto the bed, with him on top of me, pinning my hands up above my head, his weight pushing down on my lungs and making me struggle for breath. I remember his voice, over and over: "You're just a whore, aren't you? You're just a dirty little whore. Say it! Say you're a whore! Say you love it!"

I remember being terrified about having no control over what was happening, terrified he wouldn't use a condom and I wouldn't be able to stop him. I remember the moment of relief when he put one on and the immediate fear again as he started to tie my wrists together with a pillowcase. I screamed, then. I knew that once I was tied up there would be no control at all, and I struggled and flailed until he gave up. After that, he was even nastier in what he had to say.

I remember him fucking me, hard, slamming into me with a force that had more to do with rage than anything else, ramming so hard that I thought I couldn't take another stroke, the pain was so intense. He was hitting my cervix, he was ramming it so hard that I was convinced he was ripping my flesh, ripping my insides. I remember him pulling back and pushing me onto my stomach, and I remember the horror I felt as I realized that he was trying to push his way into my ass.

I'm not a prude; far from it. I've had anal sex many times and have enjoyed it. I've role-played all sorts of things that involved submission and dominance, and, with the requisite safe words in place, felt free to explore all sorts of facets of my sexuality.

But there was nothing that felt safe or free about this transaction, and I reacted intensely.

Barry was not pleased. "Hookers take it in the ass," he snarled.

"Not this one," I said.

Most people would have left it there. Most people, even people with only a modicum of social skills, would have accepted that it wasn't going to happen and would have moved on as gracefully as possible. Some might even have apologized. Later, I learned that many of Peach's girls shared my fear of having anal sex with a stranger – and particularly one who has already inflicted pain – so Barry, who had a long history with Peach, might well have known that I would refuse. He might have requested it during our brief telephone conversation. It seemed clear, now, why he hadn't. If you don't ask, no one can say no. And he just might be able to trick or force me into doing it …

AN INTERVIEW WITH
JENNY ANGELL

1. Are you still in touch with Peach, or any of the girls that you worked with during your time as a call girl? Would you now consider Peach a friend?

Only with Peach. I think that our friendship started at the heart, and has continued there, whereas what I shared with my co-workers was really firmly attached to The Work. So many so-called friendships are like that, aren't they? You're intensely involved in someone else's life because of circumstances, and when those circumstances change, the relationship does, too. And these particular circumstances – that you shared a client's bed, for example – just don't lend themselves to anything long-term.

2. How do you think your experience would have differed if it were a man setting up your appointments with clients, rather than a madam?

I don't know that I could have done it, were it a man. Peach imagined what her girls were going through, she had empathy, she cared. I'm not saying that men cannot care; but I *am* saying that men who make a living off women's work (whether those women be seamstresses in a sweatshop or sex workers in a brothel) start seeing the women in terms of hours, of income.

Plus it has to be said that Peach had this whole intimacy thing going with her clients, as well. Many of them really did think of her as a friend. They confided in her. They flirted with her. It was a special relationship to them, one that would have been impossible with a man.

3. Have you ever accidentally come into contact with a former client, and if so, how did you deal with it?

Not so much recently, but I used to occasionally see someone at an event – a concert, perhaps, or a restaurant. It was less problematic than you'd imagine, since they were a great deal less likely to want to see me than I was to see them.

4. Do you ever regret your time in the sex industry? Would you recommend it as a profession?

Very different questions, and both have, I'm afraid, both ambivalent and ambiguous answers. Do I regret it? No, of course not: it got me through a very rough patch in my life. Would I have preferred to do something else? Probably, since here in the States sex workers are regarded as somewhere below mercenaries on the scale of acceptable professions, and while I've tried to change that with these books, old prejudices don't go away. As for recommending it ... it depends so much on the context that I would hesitate to say. I worked in as safe an environment as can be possible; I know that's not everyone's experience. I worked for a woman who genuinely cared about her employees; I know that's not everyone's experience. I didn't get dragged into a lifetime of drug use; I know that's not everyone's experience.

I can't say that I'd recommend it as a *profession* in any case. It's not something that you want to do for the rest of your life – it's physically, mentally, and emotionally taxing. As a stop-gap sort of thing; that's a different story. Obviously one lasts longer as a madam than one does as a call girl, and it may be an option for more women. The goal in both cases is to legalize the profession to make it safer for everyone.

Madam

I'd like to say a little more about Peach here, since this is her book. Actually, as I write this, I'll be meeting her for lunch in Boston today. The real estate venture mentioned in the book didn't work out, but she now does sales for a company offering search engine optimization and is very happy. Her marriage is thriving; her son is happy. It's a happy ending, and I think that that's the emphasis I'd like to place here: I'm not saying that either of these professions is legal or easy, and both are best practiced on one's way somewhere else, not as an end in themselves. Someday that might change. Someday prostitution may be seen as a normal part of life in society. But until it is, sex workers of all kinds need to be protected and to protect themselves.

Enjoyed *Madam*? Prepare to be thrilled
all over again …

Callgirl

Jenny Angell

Professor by day, callgirl by night – a true story

Jenny is left penniless by an ex-boyfriend and, in order
to make ends meet, she finds herself juggling two
lives – respected college-lecturer by day and $200-an-
hour high class callgirl 'Tia' by night.

Tia's clients range from the pitiful to the downright
disturbing: there's the man obsessed with wearing her
underwear, the client who wants her to pretend to be
his mother and the punter who gets his kicks from
inflicting pain. Tia is paid to fulfil all kinds of desires.

Despite her madam's protection, Tia is drawn into a
world of increasing danger, trying to dodge under-
cover cops, resist the temptation of drugs and, most of
all, avoid falling in love with the wrong man.

As Jenny juggles the twin roles of professor and prostitute, the eventual strain of keeping her life secret from
friends and family forces her to re-examine everything –
before her two worlds inevitably collide …

ISBN: 978-1-84756-065-0